THE WHITE LADY

THE
WHITE

ILLUSTRATED BY

Leonard Dubkin

LADY

SY BARLOWE

G. P. PUTNAM'S SONS
NEW YORK

TO MY DAUGHTER

PAULINE

WHO SHARES MY INTEREST
IN NATURE

FROM THE LIBRARY OF

MARY MURRAY SCANLON

THE WHITE LADY

I

IT IS SOMETIMES DIFFICULT
to know where to begin a thing, where an experience one
wants to tell about really had its inception. Each incident that one thinks about as being the beginning is a
member of a series that goes back to some other incident,
and that goes back to still another, and thus they go back
and back until they all blend together into a hazy, in-
distinct blur in one's memory, like people marching one
behind the other over the horizon and out of sight. The
real culprit in this matter is time, or rather our concep-

tion of time, which has a habit of arranging events in an inflexible order, and keeping them that way without regard for convenience or necessity. If one could arrange one's private events as one saw fit, if one could say, first this will happen, then that, and finally the other, one might be able to arrange things in a more logical relationship. But as it is one must accept time's ordering of events, and if one should attempt to tamper with that order in the telling of a story one would certainly be stigmatized as a liar.

I suppose the story I am going to tell really had its beginning on that evening in June when, having taken my mother to visit a friend of hers, I had a few hours to kill before it was time to call for her again. I had thought of driving over to the lake shore to park the car and look out at the lake for an hour or so, and that was my intention when I drove north on California Avenue. But when I came to the bridge just north of Belmont I pulled the car over to the curb and stopped. The scene on my right looked vaguely familiar, and yet somehow different from the way I remembered it, like a picture turned upside down. There was an open field of grass and tall weeds, and back in the distance what resembled a small forest. As I sat in the car looking out of the window there came to my mind a sudden vision of myself as a boy walking through this field toward the trees beyond. But

[2]

in my memory this scene looked different, and as I turned my head and looked around now I realized that when I was a boy this bridge had not been here, and I used to cross the river on the bridge at Kedzie Avenue and walk back, and thus I approached this field from a different angle. Since then they had built this bridge across the river and made California Avenue a through street, and that brought the field right out into the open and the little forest directly behind it, instead of being secluded and inaccessible as they had been when I was a boy.

I turned my head and looked in the other direction, and sure enough there was the low, dirty, brick factory building with its six steel chimneys that towered high above the buildings and trees in the neighborhood. These high chimneys had been a landmark for me; they identified, no matter where I might be when I saw them, the field and the woods and the river here. I might be working in an office downtown, and, waiting for an elevator to take me down, I would glance out of the window and see, far off in the distance, like a black glove with six upward pointing fingers set among the low buildings of the northwest side, these chimneys writing thin pencil marks of smoke in the sky. Then for a moment I would remember the many hours I had spent here with a butter-fly net and a pair of field glasses, catching insects and

[3]

snakes and turtles, collecting birds' eggs and stones and fossils. I always thought at such times how strange it was that these six chimneys off in the distance were all that remained to me of my desire to be a naturalist, and of my youthful fervor for natural history.

Suddenly I felt an urge to walk through the field again, and between the trees. The forest, I remembered, was not really a forest at all, for when one came close to it there were only a few willow and cottonwood and oak trees set rather far apart. I took the key out of the car and walked out into the field. It was a warm evening, and the sun was hot on my back as I walked through the pathless field, stepping around clumps of thistle and trying to avoid the burrs that seemed to reach out to attach themselves to my clothes. A monarch butterfly almost brushed against my face in passing, and then I stopped when I saw a mourning cloak wheel about in the air and alight on the head of a brown-eyed Susan. I tiptoed cautiously toward it, my open hand held out ready for the capture, but just before I reached it the butterfly flew off. Well, I thought as I walked on, it was just as well. I had no box to put it in, and no collection at home in which to keep it. I looked around to see if anyone had been watching me, and though I saw no one I could not help smiling at the thought that someone might have seen me get out of my car and walk into the field, and guessed, from the clothes

[4]

I was wearing, the gray business suit, the light Panama hat, and the bow tie, that I was some sort of business-man; and then how amazed this observer would have been to see me stop and begin stalking a butterfly resting on a flower.

I walked a little farther and finally I came to something I remembered. It was a long, narrow hill about ten feet high, as far as I knew, the only elevation anywhere around here. Plants grew about halfway up its sides, but above that it was bare and white and stony, like some high mountain with its peak above the timber line. When I was a boy I used to climb this hill to look for stones and minerals and fossils for my collection, and sometimes I ate my lunch sitting on its top, from where I could see the river flowing off into the distance, and even the cars crossing the bridge at Kedzie Avenue.

I climbed up the hill and sat down on its hard white top, then took off my hat and wiped the perspiration from my forehead. It certainly was strange, I thought, that no one ever came here, that this hill and the field and woods still seemed as wild and uninhabited as they had fifteen years ago. When I was a boy this place was all but inaccessible, and I used to think of it as my own private hunting ground; now, even though a bridge had been built across the river and California Avenue was a

[5]

through street, it still seemed as lonely and as unvisited and unspoiled as it had then.

This hill that I was sitting on, I remembered having decided, was a terminal moraine, it had been left here by the ice sheet that pushed down from the arctic thousands of years ago. Idly I picked up a few of the stones lying on top of the ridge and looked at them. Yes, they were the same kind of stones I had found here when I was a boy, and added to my collection. There were pieces of red and black and orange granite, and one piece of black granite was set with a gem of milk-white quartz. There was yellow sandstone so soft that it crumbled to powder in my hand, and pieces of slate that broke into thin sheets when I picked them up. There was a stone that had square crystals of mica on its surface like tiny windows to let light into the interior, and pieces of iron pyrites that looked like snail shells and shone with a dull green brilliance in the sunlight.

And then, wonder of wonders, I picked up a stone that, when I had examined it closely, proved to be a fossil trilobite, a little sea animal somewhat like a shrimp, that has been extinct for three hundred million years. Holding the fossil in my hand I remembered how I had searched everywhere for one of these stones when I was a boy, for I had read somewhere that they were quite common in the Chicago area. I had looked for them in

[6]

abandoned quarries, on hills outside the city, and in clay riverbanks, but I had never found one. I had finally gotten one for my collection from another boy in exchange for a live turtle, but of course that was not the same as finding it myself. And all the time this fossil trilobite was lying here on this hill, and I had never seen it.

As I sat looking at the stone in my hand there suddenly swept through me an overpowering sense of bewilderment and confusion at the mixed-upness of things and the strangeness of time. Here I was sitting on a ridge of earth left here by a glacier twenty thousand years ago, holding in my hand the fossil remains of a creature that had lived three hundred million years ago, and rather sadly remembering the eager boy I had been. The whole thing seemed like a wild, pointless confusion, and chaos of years and centuries and geologic eras that could never sort themselves out in my mind.

What is time anyway, I asked myself, does it really have any existence? I had read that, according to Einstein's theory of relativity, time is relative, it varies according to the position of the observer. But wasn't that just another way of saying that time had no existence in reality, that it was a separate creation by and for each individual observer? The past was gone, certainly it had no reality except in my own mind and in the minds of other individuals; and the future was not yet, no one could say that it existed now. So the only reality was the present moment, shorn of all superstitious notions that what was now had once been something else, and would be something entirely different in the future. And in the present moment I was sitting here on a mound of earth holding a stone in my hand and thinking a thought. All the rest, the age of this mound of earth, the fact that the stone was a fossil trilobite, and the boy I was thinking about, these were illusions, they were pretty pictures I was painting in my mind to add color and significance to the events that were happening to me now.

I left the hill and walked across the field toward the woods. I had always called it the woods, but now as I walked into it I smiled at my youthful exaggeration; there were no more than a dozen trees in all, and they were scattered about with sunlight between them, and grass growing all about. I came to the oak under which, in the fall, I used to find acorns, and now I picked up a little oak apple that had fallen from the tree. I had found a few of these things when I was a boy, but I did not know what they were, and added them to my collection as curiosities. Now I knew that a certain species of wasp injected a chemical substance into the stem of the oak when she laid her eggs there, and this substance caused the stem to enlarge like a tumor around the eggs.

Suddenly, walking between the trees, I stopped and stared at a huge, round, domelike affair that surrounded the trunk of a large tree. I remembered the tree well, though it had not been so large when I was a boy. It was a locust, and every fall I used to pick up dozens of the long, black seed pods that fell from the branches, and that were filled with hard brown seeds that rattled when the pods were shaken. Now all sorts of creepers and vines had grown up from the ground and twined themselves around the bottom branches of the tree forming a dense, impenetrable mass of branches and twigs and foliage that curved upward like an igloo to a height of eighteen to twenty feet at the tree trunk. I walked completely around the whole thing looking for an opening, trying to push the branches apart so I could see inside, but the vines were so thickly entwined, around themselves and around and between the lower branches of the tree, that I could not even push my hand in, much less get in myself.

I stood for a long time staring at the structure, my mind filled with wonder that such a thing could grow up here in the city. It was certainly a natural structure that had just happened to grow in this form, it could not have been planned or built by human hands. It was the sort of thing one might believe possible in a dense forest in the tropics, but here in the city, where the soil would barely

[9]

support a little grass and a tree here and there, it was certainly strange to come upon such a proliferation of vines and creepers and other vegetation. It was useless to wonder how and when this had occurred; but was there any way I could get inside, and what would I find when I did get in?

I put my hand up as high as I could reach on top of the structure and pressed down on it. It gave only a little, and seemed strong enough to support my weight. I was determined to climb up to the top of the structure to see if there was an opening somewhere through which I could crawl, perhaps up near the trunk of the tree. Carefully I gripped the vines with my fingers and pulled myself upward, then stepped up on the mass. As I climbed upward on my hands and knees I could hear little twigs crackling and feel the vines sink like springs under my weight, but soon I located one of the branches of the tree, and I climbed up it the rest of the way to the trunk.

When I finally reached the top I stood for a moment on a branch of the tree, with one arm around the trunk, looking down at the curious structure. Yes, the vegetation was much less thick up here. There were little ragged holes in the foliage, and one large opening, about a foot in diameter and close to the trunk. Looking down through this opening I could see only darkness, there was nothing inside but a black void. Still I continued to look into the opening, there was something strangely fascinating about it; and then I became conscious of a weird sort of movement down inside the black void, a slow, weaving, undulatory movement, as though ghosts were dancing a stately minuet in the darkness under the tree. A cold chill of apprehension went through me as I continued to stare in fascinated wonder at the eerie movements in the black depths. Then suddenly I straightened up and took my eyes from the opening. Less than a hundred yards away I could see California Avenue, with cars rolling smoothly along over the bridge, and beyond that I could see the streetcars on Kedzie Avenue. Off to one side there was the squat little factory building, with smoke spiraling upward from its chimneys. What a fool I was to be afraid, to think of supernatural explanations for a movement in the dark. This was the twentieth century, I was a grown man, and I was standing on a branch of a tree in broad daylight in a modern city. What could there possibly be under the tree to frighten me?

I looked down through the opening again, and at first saw only blackness, but soon I began to perceive the movement again, the slow, rhythmic undulations inside. What could be moving about down there in the darkness? Getting down on my knees on the branch of the tree I braced myself with my hands on the vines close to the trunk and brought my face down into the opening. For a second I peered into the blackness but before my eyes could become accustomed to the darkness, before I could co-ordinate what I was seeing, there was a sudden upward rush of something into my face, cold and clammy objects struck my cheeks and forehead and nose, and a pandemonium of squeakings broke out in my ears. I lost my balance on the branch of the tree and plunged through the hole pulling leaves and twigs and stems of vines down with me to the ground under the tree.

II

WHO HAS NOT DREAMED, AT
some time or other, of falling through a hole in the
ground and finding himself in another world? This is
one of those universal daydreams that almost everyone
has experienced, either as a child or as an adult. Whenever one's everyday life has become all but intolerable,
when a request for a raise in pay has been refused or
one has been turned down by a girl, then it is pleasant
to go into a reverie and imagine oneself walking down a
path through a meadow, and suddenly falling through

a hole into a green, brilliant, beautiful world where the onerous conditions of life up above do not apply. There one can marry the king's daughter, or become a great baseball pitcher, or amass fabulous wealth, or do whatever it is that one has been unable to do in the upper, ordinary world of reality.

In my own case this daydream, which I experienced quite frequently when I was a boy, took on a slightly different form. I wanted to be a naturalist when I grew up, a famous naturalist who discovered new species of animals and formulated new theories to explain the phenomena of nature. But my mother, who did not otherwise object to my interest in nature, would not allow me to leave the city in search of rare specimens, she was afraid something would happen to me if I was away from her side for more than a few hours. And, since all the species of animals in Chicago were known, and it was highly unlikely that I could formulate any new theories of nature while wandering about the streets, I resorted to this daydream for the realization of my ambitions. When I fell through a hole in the ground into another world I always found it inhabited by strange creatures, by prehistoric brontosauri and flying reptiles, and animals without eyes, and huge, monstrous insects. No human being had ever seen this world before, and after I had examined its natural history and formulated theories to explain the things I saw there, I found my way back to the world above, and amazed the scientists with the books I wrote about my discoveries.

I remembered this childish daydream as I sat in the dimness under the locust tree after I had fallen through the hole, and it seemed like a premonition of what was happening to me now. I had landed on my back, but there was a thick carpet of leaves under the tree that cushioned my fall, and, except for a little stiffness, I was unhurt. There was a peculiar musky odor that seemed overpowering when I first sat up, but in a few minutes I became accustomed to it, and the smell did not seem so strong. But the thing that amazed me was the fact that it was not dark down here at all, the blackness I had seen when I peered down through the hole from above had become a cool, gray dimness, like a room with the shades pulled down. The late afternoon light filtered in through the foliage, and streamed down from the openings near the trunk to cast dancing little figures of light on the floor as the leaves above moved and twirled in the breeze. After I had been sitting for a few minutes I could see very plainly down here, except for the outer rim of the circular space, where the vines and creepers came down to the ground, which seemed from where I sat near the trunk of the tree to be darker than the rest of the space.

The mystery of the movement I had seen in the darkness before I fell was solved the moment I sat up and looked about me, and I could not help smiling when I recalled the eerie feelings that had gone through me as I stood on the branch of the tree looking down through the hole, and the wild, unnatural conjectures that had gone through my mind. There were bats down here, a great many of them, and though some of them had become frightened when I blocked their place of exit with my face and had flown out, others were still whirling around the trunk of the tree, squeaking as they flew. As I watched them I could see that occasionally one or two of them flew out, and others came in. There was a continual movement of bats in and out of the opening through which I had fallen. They had probably been asleep down here all day, and now they were preparing to go out, and when I had put my head down into the opening some of them had become frightened and had flown against my face in their efforts to get out.

What an amazing place this was. I thought: this natural grotto under a tree in a big city completely cut off from the outside world, where a colony of bats lived. What strange quirk of nature had fashioned it in this particular place, and how many years had it been here? I dug my hand into the vegetation on the floor of the grotto, and brought a handful of the stuff up to my eyes. It consisted of leaves and small twigs and parts of the seed pods of

[16]

the locust tree, and it had a strong musky odor, probably from the accumulated droppings of the bats. Then I dug down a little farther, and found that beneath this top layer the vegetation was ground up and indistinguishable, and it got harder and more firmly compressed the deeper into it I dug. The hole was almost two feet deep before I reached the ground, before my fingers brought up earth instead of compressed vegetation.

How many years had passed since the bottom layer of vegetation had fallen here, since the winds had blown free beneath this tree? Digging down into the floor was like an illustrated lesson in geology, like digging into the earth itself to see how forests had been compressed into veins of coals, and sand into rocks. And if I were a geologist I could read in the vegetation that had fallen here through the years, the whole history of this grotto, how long ago it had been formed, and when the bats came, and which years had been good and which lean. Now here I was again, I said to myself, remembering how only a few minutes ago I had sat on a ridge of earth holding a fossil in my hand, meditating about time; and now it did seem to exist, and the past had reality in the records it left in the earth. Did I believe that time existed, or did I think it was a mental conception of each individual? Someday I would have to make up my mind.

I got up and looked about. A few of the bats were still

flying around the trunk just beneath the top of the grotto, but most of them had gone out. I could see through the opening that the light outside was beginning to grow dim; evening was coming on, and I would have to leave soon. But first I walked around the trunk of the tree, peering here and there to see what there was to see. I came to a little ball hanging like a ripe fruit from the roof of the grotto, and I reached up my hand to pick it. Suddenly it sprouted wings, and with a little squeak flew up to join the other bats circling the tree trunk. I walked a few steps more and saw another little ball hanging, this time somewhat lower on the roof. Cautiously I tiptoed toward it, and slowly brought my hand up to the roof a few inches from the hanging bat. Then with a sudden sweep I captured it, a warm, furry little creature about two inches long that squeaked and struggled in my hand. Holding it by the back of the neck so it could not bite me I looked at it intently. This was the first time I had ever held a live bat in my hand, or had a chance to examine one at close range.

What a strange being this was, this dark-brown little mouse with big ears and thin, leathery wings. What would it be like to be a winged mouse, to hibernate all winter, sleep all day and come out at night to flit silently between the trees, to possess senses that no other beings had? A man could understand what it was like to be a bird, to be especially designed for flight, with hollow bones, stream-lined body, and wings that were clothed in light, strong feathers. But to be a mammal, to be a squeaking, furry, loathsome mouse, and to have wings of skin that could speed one through the air, over the heads of all other mammals, faster and higher and more easily than any other being could move, that was hard for a man to understand. And what do the bats think of themselves, what is their estimation of their own position in the scale of life on the earth? Certainly they consider themselves a higher form of life than all mammals that cannot fly, and to them it must seem that the aim of life and the striving of all living things is toward flight. Insects they probably consider a low order of life conceived solely as a food supply for bats; many insects were even pro-vided with wings so they could fly up to where the bats could more easily get them. But what is the attitude of bats towards birds? Some larger species of bats eat small birds, but on the other hand owls and hawks eat bats. Do the bats then think of owls and hawks and other large birds as superior beings whose wrath must be propitiated by an occasional sacrifice of one of their numbers, as primitive men thought of their gods?

Standing there under the tree holding the bat between my fingers, I noticed that the fur on the bat's stomach was moving in an unusual manner. I brought the little creature up closer to my eyes, and saw that a little baby bat, less than an inch long, was clinging tightly to the fur on her stomach. Why it should seem so strange to me that a baby bat was clinging to its mother's fur I do not know, but a sudden feeling of unearthly weirdness filled me, a feeling that I was looking at something spectral and mysterious and unfathomable. Perhaps it was the small size of the baby bat, the fact that the creature I held in my hand was herself so small that I was unprepared to find an even tinier being hanging from her stomach. At any rate, I put my finger out to touch the tiny thing, to see if it was real, and the mother, with a little squeak which I suppose denoted anger, twisted her head downward and sank her sharp little teeth into my finger tip. Of course I let go my hold on her, and she flew up, circled the tree trunk twice, and then flew out through the opening, the last of the bats under the tree.

As I watched her zoom out through the opening a hundred questions crowded into my brain. Did she always carry her baby clinging to her fur when she went out at night, and did all the females carry their young with them wherever they went? How many bats lived here under this tree, and were they all of the same species, and both males and females? Where did they go at night when they left here, and what time did they return, and how did they spend their days? Did they hibernate here in the wintertime, or did they migrate before they hibernated? As question after question flowed through my mind I began to see a great light opening up before me, like a brilliant path that beckoned me onward. Why couldn't I come here every day, or as often as possible, and study the bats that lived here, and observe them in their daily lives, and find out all I could about them? It was a golden opportunity, a chance to observe creatures that no one knew very much about. Yes, I decided, I would do it, I would start in a day or two. And the very first thing I would do would be to come here late one afternoon, about this time of the day, and spend the night under the tree, so I would be here when they returned in the morning and could watch them hang themselves up from the roof and compose themselves for sleep. And now it seemed to me that I had indeed fallen into the strange and beautiful world of my boyhood daydream, a world inhabited by marvelous creatures that I could study. And it might even be that after I had studied the bats for a while I could formulate some new theory that would startle the scientific world.

But first I must find a place close to the floor where I could get in and out. It would never do to fall or jump down from the opening in the roof every time I wanted to get in, not only because it would be inconvenient for myself, but also because it would frighten the bats. So

[21]

I walked around the grotto, peering closely at the vines and creepers close to the ground, and every time I came to a place where they were not too thick I pushed them aside with my hand. Finally I found a place where there were no branches of the tree or thick stems of vines, and breaking a few twigs and creepers, I made an opening about a foot and a half wide and pushed myself through to the outside. Under the tree I had had no idea of directions, but now when I looked around I saw that the opening I had made faced the east, toward the woods and away from California Avenue. I gathered some weeds and leafy twigs of bushes and wove them in among the other vegetation to close the opening I had made, and then I started back across the field.

When I got back to the car I looked down for the first time at my clothes. My gray suit was spotted and dirty, and I had torn my shirt on a branch when I fell into the grotto. I would have to remember to wear old clothes when I came here again, especially when I came to spend the night under the tree. But where was my hat, where had I lost it? I was sure I did not have it on when, standing on the roof of the grotto, I had peered down into the opening. Well, it was gone, and I was not going back to look for it. It was worth a hat to have discovered the grotto under the tree, and to find that it was inhabited

[22]

by a colony of bats. And it was worth many hats to have held a small, brown, furry creature in my hand, and to have felt the sense of weird unreality when I saw the tiny baby clinging to her fur.

III

BEFORE RETURNING TO THE grotto I went to the public library to get some books about bats, in order to read what was already known about them. I expected to come home with an armful of books, but the librarian assured me that only one book had ever been published on the general subject of bats. It was called simply *Bats*, and was written by a professor of Comparative Zoology at Harvard University, Glover Morrill Allen, in 1939.* The librarian also suggested

* Published by Harvard University Press.

that I read some of the articles on bats published in various scientific journals, and I spent four hours sitting at a desk in the reference room of the library, going through an index of magazine articles and reading those that referred to bats. But I found these articles neither helpful nor interesting, for most of them concerned such matters as an analysis of the structure of the teeth in the fruit-eating bat *Artibeus planirostris*, and a list of the contents of the stomachs of four cave bats *Antrozous pallidus*. Professor Allen's book on bats, however, I took home with me to read and study.

Comparing the photographs in this book with my remembrance of the bat I had held in my hand, I recognized it as a little brown bat, *Myotis lucifugus*, the most common species in the temperate regions of the United States. Since there are some two thousand species of bats in the world, and this book was a general treatment of the entire subject, the author naturally could not devote much space to any particular species, but it was apparent that *Myotis lucifugus* was his favorite among the bats. Besides the usual references to little brown bats under the various headings, there was a rather longish account of one such bat the author had kept in a cage as a pet. Peter, as Professor Allen called his pet, was fond of bluebottle flies, crickets, grasshoppers, and meal worms, but would not eat ordinary houseflies. Peter became very

tame, and would often eat out of his master's hand.
"When resting on a flat surface he had a curious spidery
appearance, supporting himself on the thumbs and tips
of the wrists, his wings folded snugly at the sides, and
his body raised on the hind feet. One morning I found
my pet dead in his box after a month in captivity."

I also learned that little brown bats will return to their
roosting place after being carried "a number of miles"
away; that segregation of the sexes occurs at certain
times, but not at others (the times when it does and does
not occur not being given); that the males become sexually active late in the fall; and that they hibernate in
caves during the winter. This was not a great deal of information; it left many gaps that I could not fill merely
by watching the bats in the grotto. But I assumed that it
was practically all that was known with any degree of
certainty about these most common of bats at the time
the book was published, in 1939.

It was not until three days after my discovery of the
grotto that I returned there to spend a night under the
tree. If I had had my way I would have come the next
day, but it took me three days to convince my mother
that I would be perfectly safe under the locust tree. She
was certain that some harm would befall me, that I would
get pneumonia, or be bitten by a snake, or hit on the head
by a thug. I am that most pitiable of beings, an only

child, and since my father's death when I was a little boy
my mother had dedicated her life to me, to keeping me
well and making me happy. But now I thought rebel-
liously, I am a grown man, twenty-seven years old, and
it is my right to live a life of my own, including the
observation of a bat colony, if I so choose. And I resolved
to be firm.

When I first told my mother about my discovery of the
grotto under the locust tree and of the bats that roosted
there, she seemed genuinely interested. Bats were such
interesting animals, she said, and they had such strange
habits, like sucking the blood of human beings while they
slept. I explained to her that while there was a species of
bat in the tropics that lived on the blood it sucked from
animals and men, the bats I had discovered had no such
habit, they lived entirely on insects they caught in the
air, and were perfectly harmless. But when I told her of
my intention of spending a night under the tree she was
horrified, and burst into tears. The next evening we spoke
of it again, and again she began to cry, and the same
thing happened on the following evening. But on the
third day I put my foot down. I insisted that tonight I was
going to sleep under the tree with the bats, in spite of
anything she might say. She tearfully made some sandwiches for me and put some coffee in a thermos bottle,
though I insisted I would not need anything to eat. She

also made me take a blanket along, and as she bade me good-by said, "Now do be careful, darling. Remember, I'll be sitting up all night waiting for you." For me, who was about to contribute at long last to the sum total of scientific knowledge!

It was eight o'clock in the evening when I left home, drove the five miles to the bridge over the river at California Avenue, parked the car and walked, with the rolled-up blanket, the paper bag of sandwiches, and the thermos bottle under my arm, across the field toward the locust tree. When I reached the tree I stood for a few minutes looking about, staring at the top of the grotto near the opening where I had seen the bats emerge, and peering up into the air and between the trees for some sign of the bats. It was just a little while before darkness would set in, and I could feel the deep, reverential hush of evening over everything, as though nature were tiptoeing about with her finger to her lips telling all the world to be more quiet. High in the air a few swallows were twittering, but I could see no bats anywhere. Could it be that I had so frightened them when I fell into their grotto that they had decided to move to a new roosting place? My heart sank at the thought.

I walked to the place where I had left the grotto, pulled aside the branches and twigs I had used to cover the opening, and crawled inside. I was about to leave the blanket outside, as I would certainly not need it to lie on; the layer upon layer of vegetation that covered the floor was as soft as any mattress. But it occurred to me that it might get cold during the night, and I could use the blanket as a cover. Until then it would serve as a pillow. So I pulled the blanket, the bag of sandwiches, and the thermos bottle inside with me, and left them lying near the opening.

After my nose had become accustomed to the musky smell, and my eyes to the dim light, I walked about under the tree, peering at the roof for hanging bats. After a time I saw one, hanging like a little pear from the vegetation, and my heart leaped up at the knowledge that they were still here, they had not deserted this grotto. When I reached for the bat it did not fly away, but crawled up and tried to hide in the vegetation, uttering a series of high, nasal, pathetic little squeaks. I caught him, and when I held him in my hand I saw that he was a young bat, not yet able to fly. He was about half the size of the bat I had held in my hand a few days before, though much larger than the tiny baby that had clung to her fur. I put him back on the roof and continued walking about, and soon it dawned on me that the place was full of young bats, some hanging by their hind feet, heads down, in characteristic bat fashion, others hiding among the vegetation, from where I would occasionally hear their squeaks, and

[30]

a few even crawling about on the floor. I counted fifty-seven, but there must have been many more in the vegetation where I could not see them, and high over my head. They all seemed to be of approximately the same size, none as tiny as the baby I had seen a few days before, nor much more than half as large as the full-grown bat.

I brought the blanket to the center of the grotto, dropped it on the ground, and sat down beside it, resting my back against the tree trunk. Well, I said to myself, I have already learned one fact about little brown bats, or at least I have surmised it. When the babies are young they are taken along by their mothers, clinging to the fur on their mothers' stomachs, when they go out at night; but after the young bats have reached a certain age they are left behind to spend the night in the roost. It was probably not only a matter of age, but of weight as well. Not only were these young bats who had been left here old enough to take care of themselves, but they were probably too heavy for their mothers to carry about all night. But did the adults spend the whole night flying about in search of insects, or did they hang themselves up somewhere, perhaps from the branch of a tree, when they got tired? Did they come back here at any time during the night to feed their young, to see that they were all right? How did the youngsters pass the time while the

[31]

parents were away? The book had mentioned a segregation of the sexes; could it be that all the adults that roosted here were females? And if so, where were the males, and when and where would they join the females? Questions crowded my mind as I sat on the floor of the grotto. Would I ever be able to answer them, would I have enough time and patience and ingenuity to ferret out some of the secrets of these mysterious little beings, to learn something of their habits and the way they lived their lives?

It was dark now, the dancing beams of light had faded from the floor of the grotto and the trunk of the tree. Blackness was everywhere. I looked up through the hole in the roof and saw that the sky too was dark, but with a lighter, softer, more velvety blackness, and from where I sat I could see a single tiny pinpoint of a star, like a diamond set in some black velvet material. In the stillness under the tree I could hear an occasional faint little nasal squeak, as though the young bats were calling to each other to keep up their courage. Once I heard a tiny thud, followed by a series of squeaks, and I guessed that one of the young bats had fallen to the floor. I fixed the blanket behind me for a pillow and lay down on the leafy floor of the grotto.

Lying there I thought of my mother at home, and I visualized her pacing the floor in the living room, wringing her hands, unable to sleep because of her fear that something would happen to me. It was not pleasant to be the recipient of so much solicitude, of so much protectiveness and anxiety that at twenty-seven an independent life was difficult. A man, it seemed to me, must not cling to his mother too long.

Finally I fell asleep, and sometime during the night I dreamed a long dream, a dream that started off pleasantly enough, but ended in such gruesome horror that it woke me up with a start. I was lying on the floor of the grotto looking up toward the roof, and it was broad daylight. I saw a leaf detach itself from the vegetation up above and float gently down to land on my chest. Then another leaf floated down, and another and another, and finally they were falling thick and fast from the roof all over the grotto. It was a very pretty spectacle, and I was greatly amused at the leaves drifting down on top of me, like snowflakes falling through still air. But after a time I began to be alarmed, for the leaves were coming down faster and faster now, and they covered me up completely, though somehow I could still see them falling from the roof. Then it occurred to me what this meant; the falling of the leaves signified that time was passing while I lay here on the floor of the grotto. Already hundreds of years had passed, and the weight of the leaves above me was pressing down on me, squeezing the breath out of me. I tried to struggle, to twist my body, to pull my arms and legs, and to strain to raise my head. But it was too late, already the weight of millions of years' accumulation of falling leaves was pressing down on me. And then, in a swift glance before I awoke, I saw myself as a fossil, a cold, hard, rigid figure of stone lying under the leaves, waiting to be discovered. It was with the horror of this image filling my mind that I awoke and sat up.

It was morning, though only a dim shadow of daylight filtered through the vegetation and danced on the floor of the grotto. I looked at my wrist watch and saw that it was four thirty-five, only a few minutes after sunrise. And the grotto was a pandemonium of squeakings, a bedlam of little darting figures with flapping wings and twisting, turning bodies. The bats were everywhere, they filled the space under the tree, zooming this way and that, dropping to the floor and shooting up again, circling round the tree trunk and flapping their wings in my face. Every one of them seemed to be squeaking, and the combination of so many squeaks was a deafening, bewildering noise in my ears.

It was strange, I thought, that they should return like this, that they should come home after a night's adventures, after ten hours of hunting insects, apparently full of energy and good spirits and joyful abandon. A few days ago when I had watched them leave for their night's hunting there had been none of this. They had circled the tree trunk silently for a time and then flown out without uttering a sound, without having indulged in a single acrobatic feat. I should have thought that now, after being all night on the wing, they would come in tired and morose, like a man coming home after a hard day at the office, and silently hang themselves up to get some rest.

As I continued to watch them I began to realize why this was so, why they left swiftly and noiselessly in the evening and returned in the morning amid all this confusion. Once I saw a bat quite close to me dive to the floor and flutter there a few seconds while a youngster that had been crawling about climbed up on her stomach; and many times I saw bats that had been circling the tree trunk stop suddenly at the roof over my head and pick up their youngsters from among the vegetation. This was accomplished by the adult flapping up to the roof, grasping the vegetation with the thumbs that protrude from the joints of the wings, then swinging her hind feet up forward to attach to the roof, which made a sort of hammock for the young bat to crawl onto. While this was going on both the bats were squeaking, though there was so much noise in the grotto it seemed almost miraculous to me

[35]

how a mother could recognize the squeaking of her own child.

So it became clear to me that all this confusion in the morning when the adults returned had a definite purpose; it was not just a lot of aimless squeaking and fluttering about. It was of course a joyous celebration of the homecoming of the mothers, and their being reunited with their children, but more than that it was children calling to their mothers, and the mothers trying to recognize their children's voices and find them. So this was another fact I had discovered about little brown bats. And now as I watched the throng of bats going around the tree trunk it seemed to me that I felt very close to these alien beings, that I could sympathize with them and know how they felt. I knew how these mother bats felt when, after having been out hunting insects all night, they returned to the grotto to find their children safe and sound, and calling for them; and I could identify myself with the young bats, who had spent the long night crawling about among the vegetation or on the floor, and now heard their mothers calling to them, and saw them hang themselves up like hammocks and invite their children to come and partake of the delicious warm milk from their bulging breasts. No wonder there was so much squeaking and flapping about and confusion. It would be strange if it were otherwise.

For almost an hour I sat watching the bats circling the trunk of the tree, and by that time there were only a few left in the air. Most of them had found their young and were already hanging with them from the roof. I got up and walked about the grotto, looking as closely as I could at the bats hanging head downward. They did not seem to be spread haphazardly all over the roof, but were hanging in groups of twenty or thirty. If I approached a group too closely the bats would take off and go circling around the tree trunk again, but after a few circuits they would come back and hang themselves up. If I moved away while they were in the air they would come back to the same perch, but if I remained motionless they would hang themselves up somewhere else. I suppose the weight of the young kept them from flying for any great length of time, but occasionally one of the mothers would fly to the ground and leave her squeaking child on the floor, circle the grotto for a few minutes, then pick up her child and return to her perch on the roof. As far as I could determine almost every adult bat that I saw had a child clinging to her fur, and I do not believe there were many males or childless females in the grotto at this time.

I stood in the center of the grotto, beside the tree trunk, until the bats were all composed, until there was no more flying about and no squeaking and I presumed they were asleep. Then I tried to count them. This was very difficult because some were hanging from the roof near the edge of the grotto, close to the floor and almost out of sight, while others hung in groups high over my head and so close together that it was hard to tell how many there were in each group. But there were not less than two hundred and twenty, and I do not believe there were more than two hundred and sixty. Having completed this estimate I picked up my blanket, retrieved the bag of sandwiches and thermos bottle, and left the grotto, disturbing only a few bats which had been hanging close to the exit.

IV

ALL THE REST OF THAT SUMMER
I came to the grotto to watch the bats, sometimes two or
three times a week, but at least once a week. A few times
I spent the night under the tree to watch the bats come
in at dawn, but usually I came just before evening and
sometimes I did not go into the grotto at all, but sat
outside waiting for the bats to come out. A few times I
came at night to see how the young bats behaved while
their mothers were away, but by the last week in July
such nighttime visits to the grotto were fruitless, for all

the young bats had learned to fly and were out chasing insects with their parents, and the grotto was as silent and empty as a deserted house.

I said the young bats had learned to fly, but this is not quite accurate; I do not believe there is any learning involved, and I am sure that the mother makes no effort to teach her youngster the rudiments of flight. The process is nothing whatever like that of a young bird learning to fly, when both parents urge the fledgling to try his wings, tempt him with bits of food held just beyond his reach, and perhaps even push him off his perch if he seems too hesitant. But a young bat, when his wings are properly formed and the muscles of his arms and fingers co-ordinated, takes to the air as naturally as a baby duck to water. He requires neither instruction nor urging. But then birds are comparative newcomers to flight, whereas bats had been flying for millions of years before ever a feather made its appearance on the earth. This probably has something to do with the fact that bats are much more at home in the air than birds, it is much more nearly their natural element.

I do not mean to imply that young bats do not go through a period of trial and practice before learning to fly, that they crawl about until their wings and muscles are properly formed and then suddenly take to the air. As I observed in the grotto, during the three or four

[40]

weeks before a young bat is able to fly, he crawls about among the vegetation on the roof, hangs himself up occasionally by his hind feet, or swings by his thumbs. At least half a dozen times a day he either falls or purposely drops to the floor, and during each such fall he flaps his wings, whether to break the impact of his fall or in a conscious effort at flight, I do not know. Eventually he finds that his wings will carry him through the air, and he goes around the tree trunk a few times and then lands on the floor to rest.

It is only a day, at most two days, after a young bat has succeeded in his first flight around the tree trunk, that he accompanies the adults when they leave the grotto in the evening. And he does not come back until the rest of them return in the morning. Are his wings already capable of supporting him all night long as he flaps through the darkness, diving down and zooming up as he chases night-flying insects, dodging this way and that to avoid the branches of trees and wires and chimneys? This is possible, of course, but it does not seem likely to me. It may be that when the bats leave the vicinity of the grotto, at about nine thirty every evening, they go somewhere to rest, to some secluded, secret place where they can all hang themselves up for an hour or so. But I have never been able to substantiate this theory of mine. I only know that every evening, between nine and nine thirty, the bats vanished completely from the vicinity of the grotto. They disappeared so suddenly and completely that there was not a single bat left between the trees or in the air over the field. And they did not return until dawn the next morning, until it was time to hang themselves up and go to sleep under the tree. Where and why they went, and what they did there, I have not the slightest notion, nor whether they remained together as a group, or separated, each bat going off by himself. I have roamed about in every direction from the locust tree after the bats have left, but I have never seen any sign of them.

This, then, is the chronology of the bats' evening, as I was able to observe it in the grotto. At about seven o'clock the sleeping bats under the tree began to wake. They yawned and stretched, and uttered a few sociable squeaks, and left the perch from which they had hung all day to circle about the tree trunk. Within fifteen minutes every bat old enough to fly was on the wing in the grotto, diving and zooming and zigzagging this way and that, and stopping abruptly in mid-air to avoid collisions. There was neither order nor regularity in their flight, some flew around the tree clockwise and others counterclockwise, some were up near the roof and others seemed to be scraping the floor.

This seems strange to me, that creatures as high in the evolutionary scale, as sociable and gregarious as these

[42]

little bats, sleeping and eating and hunting together, leaving the roost together every evening and returning to it every morning in the same way, should yet have no order in their flight, no leader to guide them. Men and other gregarious animals move across the earth in armies or herds, usually with a leader; ducks and other gregarious birds fly in formation, in a prearranged order; even ants and other social insects move in swarms or armies, or travel one behind the other. But bats in the air are always individualists, and whether they are circling in a small space, as under a tree, or wheeling about beneath the sky, each bat flies as he sees fit, in any direction, at any speed and altitude he pleases. These little brown bats have carried to its ultimate degree the concept of freedom of action, of individuality, and yet they have retained the social cohesion and the neighborliness of gregarious beings. It seems to me that it might be appropriate to say to the man who is unhappily enmeshed in the taboos of tradition and custom, "Go to the bat, thou slave."

While the bats are circling the trunk of the tree there are occasional sorties by a few of them, usually three or four individuals at a time but sometimes as many as twenty, out into the open air. Watching from the outside I will see a few bats shoot upward from the opening on top of the grotto, wheel about in the air for half a minute or so, and then dive back in. Whether they come out to see if the coast is clear, if it is safe for the others to emerge, or how far down toward the horizon the sun has set, I do not know. Perhaps they merely came out because the crush inside was becoming too great, or maybe there is no reason at all for their emergence. At any rate, for ten or fifteen minutes there is a periodic in-and-out movement of a few bats, and then suddenly, as though a bell had rung or a signal had been given, there is a rush of wings upward from the opening as the whole flock swarms into the air.

I have seen this sudden rush of bats upward and outward many times, though I have sat outside the grotto waiting for it to happen and missed it probably as often. It was a momentary thing, it lasts a second, perhaps even less, but each time I see it I tell myself it was worth coming out here for, it was worth the drive in the car, the long wait while I sat on the grass at a little distance from the tree, with my eyes glued to the top of the grotto. At first there is nothing, there is only the grotto with the locust tree rearing upward from the center of the domelike structure. Then suddenly, for a fraction of a second, the grotto erupts, it belches up through its top a thin black stream, like a single puff of black smoke shooting upward from the chimney of a locomotive. So much like a puff of smoke does it appear that I am always surprised

at the absence of an accompanying sound. I always expect to hear a loud chug or a boom, as in a locomotive.
Only two or three feet above the top of the grotto the
black puff rises, and then, as though a high wind were
blowing it about, it becomes dispelled, in disperses in all
directions, and resolves itself into a myriad of individual
pairs of wings beating the air. Only as long as it takes
them to get out of the grotto do the bats fly in a swarm;
as soon as they are outside they revert to their normal
habit of flight, winging in any direction, speed, and altitude their fancy dictates.

Now the bats fill the air in the space between the trees
and over the field, skimming low above the ground,
shooting upward and zooming down, twisting and turning
and indulging in all sorts of acrobatics. They do not fly
very high, perhaps thirty feet at most, for these bats are
a low-flying species, and get their food from among the
flies and bees and grasshoppers and beetles and butter-
flies and moths that flutter just above the ground. Most
of them begin hunting immediately, but a few fly straight
to the river for a drink of water. Watching a bat take a
drink in the river is a beautiful sight, like reading a delicate little poem written on the water. I have seen birds
take a drink on the wing, swallows and swifts and gulls
and terns, but their method is crude compared to that of
the bats. A swallow, for example, will skim low over the

water, dip his beak in, leaving a V-shaped wake as though a tiny boat had traveled there, and then zoom upward. If he is still thirsty he will circle about, come back, and repeat the process. But a bat taking a drink rides along on the air a fraction of an inch above the water, his wings vibrating gently, and every foot or so he sticks his tongue down and laps up some water. Behind him as he skims along he leaves a series of little expanding ripples where his tongue dipped into the water, and it always seems to me that he is flying along dropping tiny pebbles, or perhaps sowing seeds in the river.

I have always thought it strange that people do not come to California Avenue at this time of the evening to watch the bats hunting and drinking and disporting themselves outside their roost. There must be some who see them, for the air is saturated with their bodies, and they even spill over the edge of the field at California Avenue to hunt on the other side. Cars are continually passing in both directions, and occasionally a couple walks along the pavement on their way to a movie or a store. But I have never seen a car stop while the occupant marveled at the great number of bats in the air, nor have I ever seen a pedestrian pause as he passed the field and turn his head to look at the swarm of bats. I suppose if anyone but me has seen them he has thought they were birds preparing to roost for the night, and even if he

[46]

knew they were bats he might not think it worth his while to stand there for ten minutes looking at them.

I think it is unfortunate that people are not more interested in bats, and in the spectacle that occurs every evening just east of California Avenue, for they are missing an aerial circus full of marvelous feats, of daring stunts, and of hairbreadth escapes. Often a bat will dive into the grass in pursuit of some insect, or shoot straight up into the air after a swift-flying bee. Sometimes a bat will flutter from side to side through the weeds behind a little blue butterfly, or dive straight at the trunk of a tree to pick off a resting fly. I have seen three or four of them dive at the same insect, and have held my breath in the certain belief that they were going to meet head on in a rending crash. But somehow they never collide; they swerve suddenly at the crucial moment and go off in different directions.

I believe it is generally conceded by naturalists that bats are, on the whole, more skillful flyers than birds. The most expert flyers among the birds are the swifts, and yet there are bats that can outfly the swifts both in speed and in maneuverability. This is not surprising when one considers the differences in wing structure of birds and bats. The essential parts of a bird's wing are composed of feathers, and the only control the bird has over these feathers is the ability to turn them slightly and to spread groups of them more or less. Thus the wing of a bird in flight is almost as rigid as the wing of an airplane, for in a plane too, the pilot can only control the raising or lowering of the ailerons a few inches. But the wing of a bat is skin spread along his arm and between his fingers, and he can control any part of it as easily as a man can bend his fingers. He can flap the whole wing or any part of it, he can change the lift, the pitch, or the angle of any part of it, he can alter it in any way he pleases while in flight merely by bending an elbow or moving a finger. So that while there are birds with highly specialized wings fitting them for a particular kind of flight, as humming birds for stationary flight and hawks for gliding, the bats are, by and large, more skillful in the air because their wings are more flexible—and perhaps also because they have been flying for a few million years longer than the birds.

For about two hours the bats fill the air outside the grotto, hunting insects, going to the river to drink, and, I suppose, playing about in some bat games. I have never been able to see in what direction they go. I only know that they are present one minute, and the next minute I no longer see their dark little forms flashing through the gloom. Where can they go and why do they always leave so punctually, as though they had a rendezvous to keep? Could it be that they have exhausted the supply of insects near the grotto and have gone to another feeding ground? But surely this would not happen every night at the same time, and it would be earlier in June, later in August, when swarms of insects are everywhere. Do they go to meet the males, and fraternize with them for the rest of the night? I do not think so, for the book on bats that I got from the library states that the males do not become sexually active until late in the fall, and it seems to me these mothers have more sense than to go chasing after a lot of sexually inactive males. At any rate, where-ever they go and whatever they do there, they do not come back to the grotto until the sky between the six high chimneys has begun to lighten in anticipation of the com-ing of another day.

V

DURING THE FIRST PART OF AU-
gust I began to notice an increase in the number of bats
that hung from the roof of the grotto during the day. The
young were by this time all weaned. They hung with their
mothers in the grotto by day and went out to hunt with
them by night. They had grown until they were now approximately the same size as their mothers, and it was
no longer possible to tell, even when I held a bat in my
hand, whether it was an adult or one of the young born
early in the summer. But the proportion of males in the

total bat population seemed to be rising, for almost every time I caught a bat in my hand it was a male. I counted them again one day toward the end of August, and found that there were more than six hundred and fifty bats hanging from the roof.

So there was no doubt in my mind that the males had come to join the females. Where had they been all this time, while the females gave birth to their young and raised them to adult bathood? And why had they come to join their mates now, when the work and the responsibilities of parenthood were done with, and the summer was almost over? The answers to these questions probably had something to do with procreation, with the fact that the males were now sexually active, as the book put it. But as yet I saw no sign of any activity of this sort, no copulation, no pairing off, no courtship of any kind. The males simply hung in the grotto beside the females all day, and went out hunting with them at night.

It was not until the second week in September that I saw any signs of sexual activity. I came into the grotto at about two o'clock one afternoon, and almost immediately became aware of a sort of nervous tension among the inhabitants. It pervaded the space under the tree like an electric current. Bats in pairs, always one behind the other, zipped nervously back and forth in the grotto, then suddenly hung themselves up from the roof. This went

[52]

on all the rest of the afternoon. At a time when the bats usually were asleep, they were chasing one another about the grotto. Finally at about five o'clock I succeeded in observing the beginning of one of these races, for it took place beside me as I sat on the floor.

A row of bats was hanging from a small twig growing out of one of the branches of the locust tree, and apparently they were all asleep; they hung motionless with their eyes closed. Then the bat next to the end, which I presumed to be a male, turned his head to look at the end bat, who hung no more than a foot from my head, and began edging slowly toward her. She retreated a few steps, but this was bringing her closer to my head than she cared to be, so she turned her head toward the male, opened her mouth to show her sharp little teeth, and squeaked at him. He opened his mouth and squeaked too, but he kept edging toward her, moving one little hind foot at a time on the twig above them. Finally, she let go her hold on the twig and leaped off into space; he followed behind her, zigzagging around the tree. Finally they hung themselves up somewhere else, so I did not see the end of the chase.

Three days later, when I next visited the grotto, the nervous tension was gone, and the whole place was pervaded by an air of quiet calmness, as though the bats were all asleep. But most of them were not asleep, they hung in groups of twos engaged in courtship, or were hiding among the vegetation of the roof copulating. I sat down on the floor where the roof was just over my head and watched a pair of lovers.

The pair I had selected for observation hung side by side, so close together that their wings touched, like a boy and a girl holding hands. They licked each other with long red tongues—the head, the neck, the body, and the sex organs, first one end and then the other. Then the male let go his hold on the roof with one leg, twisted his body until he faced the female, and put one wing around her, exactly like a boy putting his arm around a girl to kiss her. But what a strange position to be making love in, I thought, hanging head downward by their hind feet, like trapeze artists in a circus. Now the male had let go his hold on the roof altogether, twisted himself around onto the female's back and began to copulate. Then the female did a strange thing. She put her wings up to the roof, grasped the vegetation with her thumbs, and pulled herself, with him still on her back, up among the vegetation. Was it modesty that made her want to hide herself while engaged in the sex act or did she prefer to copulate in some other position than hanging by her heels from the roof?

Now, though there was copulation going on all over the grotto, mostly among the vegetation of the roof, the

young bats would not be born until the following spring,
for according to the book I had read, the male sperm lies
inactive in the uterus of the female all winter long, and
does not fertilize the ovule until the following spring. So
the male sperm lives the same sort of life that the male
bat had lived—a long period of inactivity, of resting and
waiting, and then a sudden short burst of energy, of fulfillment. The book did not mention it, but there is probably no ovule to be fertilized when the sperm finds itself
in the uterus of the female bat; the egg will not make its
appearance until spring. So the sperm has no choice in
the matter, its inactivity is forced on it by the conditions
of its environment. This is remarkable because the sperm
of no other mammal can survive for more than a day or
two, much less six months. And is it not at least possible
that the sexual inactivity of the male bats during the
spring and summer is due to the same condition that
affects their sperm? They are inactive because the females are all somewhere else raising their young, and
there is nothing to be active with. Since bats have not yet
reached the stage in their progress where they can find
other outlets than intercourse for their sexual needs, the
males must wait until the fall, when they join the females,
to become sexually active.

During the last few days of September and the beginning of October I noticed among the bats in the grotto a

strange condition of lethargy. It was as though chloroform had been released under the tree and the occupants were becoming drugged. None of the bats was very active. They slept more soundly during the day, and their time for leaving the grotto got later and later, their time for returning earlier. Where earlier in the summer a bat would fly away when I came too close to his resting place on the roof, or reached up my hand for him, now I could walk about the grotto in midday without disturbing them, and sometimes I could pick a bat off the roof and hold him in my hand for a minute before he awoke. I knew what this strange condition was; it was the torpor of hibernation. It was a foretaste, a sample, and a warning that soon the long winter sleep would be upon them, and the time had come to prepare for it.

I sat in the grotto one day with the sleeping bats hanging from the roof all about me, and became absorbed in meditation about the odd, bizarre, fantastic lives these little creatures lived. It would not have seemed so strange if they were a different sort of animal, if they were fish or snakes or something far removed from man. I had never thought it strange that turtles and frogs hibernated during the winter, or that insects spent the cold months as pupae, and emerged in the spring in an entirely different form from their larval stage. Turtles and frogs and insects were alien beings, they were so different from

[56]

myself that I did not expect them to lead the same sort of life that I led, just as one does not expect people on the other side of the world to have the same habits as oneself. But bats are mammals, they are almost our next door neighbors in the line of evolutionary descent. And yet their lives are so different from ours, they sleep all day and hunt all night, they are sexually inactive except during a short period in the fall, the males and the females live apart during the spring and summer, and all winter long they sleep in a state of lethargic torpor. I had associated with these bats in the grotto the entire summer, and I had come to think of them as a tribe of little people whose habits and customs might be different from mine, but who nevertheless were like me in many respects. But now this strange sleepiness was upon them, and they did not seem like the same bright, active, intelligent little beings I had known all summer.

What was time like to these bats, I wondered, and were they conscious of their long heritage of unchanging behavior, of the millions upon millions of winters that their ancestors had slept through? If time is different for each individual observer according to his frame of reference, in other words, according to where in the history of the world he is standing, then perhaps it is different for each species of animal according to how long he has been what he is. And if this is true, then to bats time is a long, slow, an almost stationary process, like a stream that has been dammed up and is becoming stagnant. There is no necessity for the hurry and rush that most other forms of life indulge in, no need for continual adjustment to change, because there is never any change. For millions of years one summer has followed another with only a short sleep between, and one night is separated from another only by a nap. There are few enemies on the earth, there has never been any competition for night-flying insects, and the wings evolved by the first primordial bats are still the most efficient on earth. So time stands still, and what bat would want it otherwise?

By the second week in October the bats hardly left the grotto at all. A few of them at a time would fly out now and then during the night and return in less than an hour to hang themselves up on the roof and go back to sleep. I began to think that perhaps they might hibernate right here under the tree, and I could come to see them occasionally during the winter. Then, on October 17, I came to the grotto in the morning and found it vacant. It was a cold, raw, windy day with an overcast sky, and so many of the leaves had fallen from the vines and branches that formed the grotto that in many places one could see into it from the outside. Inside the grotto the wind whistled and whined, and the newly fallen leaves and twigs and locust seed pods crackled and crunched under my feet as

[58]

I walked about looking for the bats. But there was not one left. They had all gone away, probably sometime during the night, for I had been there the evening before. How far did they have to travel to the place where they hibernated, I wondered. The book had said, in a blanket statement that referred to all species of bats, that they hibernated in caves. But there were no caves near Chicago. As far as I knew the nearest caves were in Missouri and southern Indiana, more than three hundred miles away. And wherever they had gone to hibernate, would they return again next spring? There was still so much I wanted to know about them, so many questions they had left unanswered.

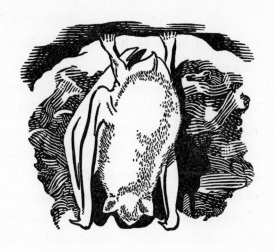

VI

THE LONG WINTER MONTHS
passed slowly that year. It seemed to me they would
never come to an end. Not once during the winter did I
go out to visit the grotto, though I would have liked to see
what it looked like with the snow piled high on top of it,
and the branches of the locust tree bare. But I reasoned
that I had spent so much time watching the bats all summer, and, if they came back next spring, I intended to
spend as much, if not more, time watching them next

summer, I ought to devote at least the winter to being with my mother.

My mother was very bitter about my neglect of her all summer long, she never missed an opportunity of reminding me how unnatural it was for a man to spend so much time with a lot of bats while he left his own mother alone. How often I heard her say on the telephone to one of her friends "My darling son is going to the bats." She always laughed when she said this, and I knew that to her the statement seemed accurate both in the literal sense and in the implication that I was becoming mentally deficient. For why would a sane man want to spend so much time watching a lot of bats, why would anyone in his right mind sit hour after hour, day after day, and night after night observing little animals that no one else was interested in?

I have asked myself that question a number of times, and I can truthfully say that I have no idea what the answer is. I had no intention of making any use, or deriving any profit from my knowledge of the habits of little brown bats. I did not actually believe I could become an authority on the subject of bats, nor had I any thought, at the time, of writing a book about them. If I were the boy I had once been I might have daydreamed of discovering in the behavior of the bats the working of some new and world-shaking scientific theory; but I was a man now,

[62]

and I knew that scientific theories were not formulated while sitting in a grotto watching bats fly around a tree trunk.

I was not naïve enough to believe that I was observing in the grotto something that had never been seen before, or even something that had never been recorded. The little brown bats are the commonest species in this country. They fly into people's homes and roost in barns and attics, and almost anyone who cares to waste a few hours can watch them. All the habits and the traits of behavior that I was discovering for myself had probably been observed thousands of times before, often by trained scientists who knew how to interpret these things. It was true that I had only been able to find one book on the subject of bats in the public library, but there were probably hundreds of chapters in scientific books devoted to them, and thousands of articles in magazines. No, it could not be that the habits and the mode of living of a creature as common as the little brown bat should be unknown to science.

Why, then, was I so intent on learning all I could about the bats in the grotto, why did I spend so much time watching them? Maybe it was because they seemed to me such mysterious little beings and I had read almost nothing about them before I discovered them. Every habit and trait mannerism I observed, every trick of flight and

[63]

manner of landing and taking off was something new to me, something unheard of. Then too, in watching them, there had grown in me an affection for these little flying mice stronger than any I had felt for any other animal. They were so marvelously efficient, so fearless and self-reliant and happy and free, and so beautiful in flight, that I could think of no more pleasant way of spending my time than to sit in the grotto or just outside it watching them, to meditate on the long history of their evolution, to become imbued with their philosophy, with their way of looking at life, and to feel, even if only for a moment, like one of them, like a tiny furred mammal with wings of skin and the freedom to fly about wherever I pleased.

I visited the grotto twice in April, when the locust tree was still bare and there were only buds and a few new leaves on the vines and creepers. But the bats had not come back. I could see through the stems and the few leaves that formed the roof, without bothering to go inside, that the grotto was uninhabited. The second time, on April 29, when I saw that the grotto was still empty, I all but gave up hope. Surely they would have returned by this time if they were coming back at all. They had probably found some new roosting place closer to the caves where they hibernated, some place where they could conduct their affairs without the nuisance of having a lone human being prying into their lives.

Just to make sure that they were not coming back, I returned again on the afternoon of May 8. Now the locust tree was in bud, and the vegetation on the roof of the grotto had grown to such an extent that it was no longer possible to see inside. I went to my old entrance, pushed aside the vines, and crawled in. At once the musky smell filled my nostrils, and my heart beat faster; but then I reasoned that the smell was probably left over from last year. I walked to the center of the grotto, looking intently up at the roof. But there was nothing, no sign of the bats anywhere, and my heart sank as I realized that now it was certain they were not coming back. Dejectedly I walked around the trunk of the tree, and suddenly there was a spurt of activity, a rush of dark wings fanning the air, so unexpected that I reeled back on my heels as though a bomb had exploded in front of me. How my spirits soared as I watched the bats I had frightened from their perch flying around the tree trunk, how I rejoiced at the thought of another summer of watching them. Yes, they had come back, but not very many of them. Sitting on the floor of the grotto after the bats had hung themselves up again, I counted twenty-six, all bunched together in a small space on the roof, as though they were afraid to separate. Would the others come back too, or would these twenty-six bats be the only inhabitants of the grotto this summer?

Later, sitting outside, I watched them emerge for their night's hunting. They came out in a stream again, all together, but of course it was not as impressive as when there had been more than two hundred bats. Instead of a sudden puff of black smoke erupting from the top of the grotto, there was only a thin trickle of black that spread out and became dissipated almost before I had a chance to see it. They hunted for insects between the trees and over the field, just as they had done last year, but now, with so few of them present, it was almost impossible to watch their antics, and sometimes I did not see a bat in the air for five or ten minutes. At nine thirty they disappeared, just as they had disappeared every night at the same time last year.

It was not until a week later that I went to the grotto again, and discovered they were all back, all that had been here last year and more. It was difficult to make an accurate count of their number, for they seemed more active than I had ever seen them before. They kept flying up in bunches of twenty or more to go circling around the tree trunk, and changing from one perch to another as though they were trying to decide which position in the grotto suited them best for a permanent perch. After trying to count them a number of times, I finally estimated

[66]

350

that there were approximately three hundred and fifty. This estimate pleased me greatly. It was exactly what I would have expected if I had been sure they were coming back. Last June, before the males had joined them, there had been about two hundred and fifty. If each of those females had given birth to one young bat, and half of these young had been females, there should now be about three hundred and seventy-five female bats. A few of the older bats had probably died during the winter, and so now the females of last summer plus the females born last spring had returned to the grotto. But it was staggering to think of the colony increasing each year in geometrical ratio, and coming back to the grotto year after year. Next summer there would be five hundred females, and the year after seven hundred and fifty, and the year after that eleven hundred. Surely there would not be room under this locust tree for eleven hundred bats, to say nothing of the males when they came.

The next day I went to the grotto again, and I brought a butterfly net with me. It was hard to catch the bats by hand, even in the daytime when they were supposed to be asleep, and I often got bitten in the process. With the net I could catch three or four at a time by merely pushing the net suddenly in front of them as they flew around the tree trunk. Then, holding the wings of one of the bats together from the outside of the net, I inserted my other

her?

doesn't
he
get to
know
individual
bats?

hand in, grasped the fur on the back of her head so she could not bite my fingers, and lifted her out. The captured bat always squeaked pitifully while I held her in my hand, and this seemed to excite the other bats, they whirled around the tree trunk, continually being joined by more and more of the hanging bats, all squeaking loudly as though in sympathy with their captured sister. But when I opened my hand and released my captive she flew up with the others, and soon the excitement and the squeaking subsided and the bats returned to their perches on the roof, and in a few minutes they were apparently asleep.

It seems strange to me that the bats did not leave the grotto permanently after I discovered it and began spending so much time there. It must have been very annoying to them to have me about at all hours, crawling in and out, catching them in a net and holding them in my hand, disturbing their sleep, and interfering with their lives. I can think of no other wild birds or animals that would have allowed such intimacies from a human being, especially at the critical period when the young were being born. But who can really know what the bats in the grotto thought of me, and why they put up with my interference? If their intelligence was equal to that of primitive human beings they might have thought of me as some sort of god, a mighty being who must be allowed to have his way.

[68]

On the other hand, it may have been that they had no place else to go, that roosts like this were rare and not to be abandoned lightly. Where else in all this part of the country could three hundred and fifty bats find refuge during the day, with a hunting ground just outside and a river close by?

I caught a number of the bats with the net, and examined them carefully. Of more than twenty that I held in my hand, all were females, and one already had a young bat clinging to the fur on her stomach. It must have been only a day or two old, for it was a tiny thing and its eyes were not yet open. I was anxious to see a bat born, to watch the process of birth in these little mammals, and I also wanted to watch a single individual from birth at least until it was able to fly, to observe it in the various stages from babyhood until it took its place in the colony with the other adults. But how I was going to do this I had as yet no idea.

In the first place, all the bats looked alike to me. I had not been able to find a single individual with any apparent difference from all the others, either in flight or when I held her in my hand. They were all dark brown in color, some darker than others, some almost black, but with so many individuals of each shade that I could never have picked out one from all the others. They were all about the same size, and all had round ears that stood up from their heads, thin wings a little darker than the rest of their bodies, sharp, white, needlelike teeth, and tail membranes of skin stretched between the hind legs. They seemed to me far more alike than any peas in a pod.

If I could have been sure that the same bats came back to the perch they had left on the roof day after day, my task would have been simplified. But I was never sure of it. Sometimes I thought I saw a particular bat come back to the same perch a number of times, and then again, when I concentrated my attention on a single individual, it often seemed to me that she hung herself up, after flying around the tree trunk, somewhere else than on the perch she had left. I knew that they favored certain spots on the roof, that they hung in groups of twenty or thirty in the same places on the roof day after day; but I did not know whether the same individuals came back to the same places.

And yet it seemed to me essential that I should pick out an individual bat that I could identify, and concentrate my attention on it. All last summer I had watched them as a mass of flying mammals, as a colony. I knew how the colony spent its days and, except for the time between nine thirty in the evening and dawn, what it did at night. Unless I could pick out an individual bat and watch it, this summer would be the same as last, a repetition of everything I had already seen, and I would learn nothing new. No, I was determined that this summer I would descend from the general to the particular, from the colony to the individual bat.

But how was I to go about this? How was I to follow a single individual when the young were all born at about the same time and looked exactly alike, and the mothers all looked alike? I had thought of various ways I might mark a young bat to identify it, but none of them seemed very promising. It would be useless to put a band around its leg, as one could do with a bird, because unless one knew exactly where to look for it one could never find a bat with a band on its leg among the hundreds in the grotto. Besides, the band would not be visible in flight, and for all I knew a young bat or its mother could easily bite through a metal band. The only method that seemed practicable was to paint some part of the young bat's body, perhaps the tail membrane, or one wing, or the fur on the stomach, with white paint. The paint would probably wear off in a short time, or the mother might lick it off the first day, and either become ill or die. But it was the only method I could think of that might succeed, and so I decided to try it. I bought a little jar of white vegetable dye, which would be less harmful than paint if it were licked off, and a small paint brush, and secreted them in a corner of the grotto, just under the roof, to await the time when I would need them.

For the next four days I went to the grotto, every day, and wandered about slowly under the tree, peering at the bats. Many of the females had already had their babies, and a few of the young were old enough to hang from the roof beside their mothers, like grapes hanging beside plums. Then, on May 28, I finally met with success. I saw a female about to give birth to her young. It was raining outside, a light, persistent drizzle, but under the tree it was dry and comfortable. During a heavy rain streams of water cascaded down from the roof, and the bats were almost constantly on the move, whirling about the grotto in search of a dry perch. But when the rain was light, as today, the only water entering the grotto came in through the opening on top, splashed against the trunk of the tree, and trickled down the bark to lose itself among the dead leaves on the floor.

It was a Sunday, and I had left home just after lunch, arriving at the grotto at about two. Wandering about inside looking at the hanging bats I came across one that was hanging from the roof in a peculiar position. The other bats all hung by their hind feet, head downward, but this one was clutching the vegetation with her thumbs, and her feet were clawing the air. She was right side up for me, her head was up and her feet were down, in the same position I would be in if I were hanging by my hands from a branch; but she was upside down for a bat,

[72]

and I had become so accustomed to seeing them hanging head downward that now she looked grotesque and unnatural, like a man standing on his hands.

When I came close to her she did not fly away, but continued to hang from the roof by her thumbs, her feet clawing the air. Except for her feet she was motionless, and no sound came from her, though her lips were bared and I could see her bright little teeth moving, as though she were gritting her teeth in pain. After a few minutes she bent her feet up under her body, so that the tail membrane stretched between them curled under her body like a pocket to receive the young bat. Soon a tiny pair of white feet emerged out of the dark fur at the bottom of her body, and these were followed by a white tail membrane, then a bare white little body, and finally a pair of white wings that were crumpled around the head. It lay now in the cradle of its mother's tail membrane, silent and motionless, still attached to its parent by the thin, white umbilical cord. Was it alive, or was it stillborn? It looked like a tiny dead white mouse, hairless and wrinkled, its wings wrapped around its head. Now the mother brought her head down and began to lick it with her tongue, turning it over and over in its cradle, licking it up and down and across and over. Suddenly it began to squeak, a thin, high, nasal squeak that was barely audible, muffled as it was by the wings. Now it was moving, it

[73]

twisted about in its cradle, brought one wing down to its side and then the other, revealing a white head which the mother immediately began to lick.

In a little while the newly born bat began crawling up out of its cradle, hooking its thumbs into the fur on its mother's stomach, and pulling itself shakily upward toward her breasts. But before it could reach its destination it was stopped short by the umbilical cord to which it was attached. It began to squeak again, louder and with pitiful urgency. The mother bent her head and grasped the baby by its neck, exactly like a cat picking up her kitten, then put it down on its back in her tail membrane. Then she bit through the umbilical cord, picked the baby up by the back of the neck again, and placed it on her stomach, its face touching the nipple of one of her breasts. While it was suckling, the placenta emerged, and the mother reached down over her child, crumpled the afterbirth into a small wad and swallowed it. This done she pulled her body up and grasped the roof with her feet, and, hanging head downward now like the other bats, she crossed one wing over the front of her body, like a woman pulling her coat around to keep her baby warm. The whole series of events, from the first emergence of the baby's feet to the mother's turning upside down, had taken four minutes.

For the first time I began to wonder about the fact that

the baby bat had been born completely white, with not a spot of brown on it anywhere. At the time I was observing its birth I had not attached any significance to this fact; this was the first bat whose birth I had watched, and I supposed they were all born white like this one, and acquired their brown coloring afterward. But now that I thought about it, it seemed singularly strange. I had already seen a number of baby bats clinging to their mothers' fur with their eyes still closed, probably only a day or two old, and there was no white on their bodies, they were exactly the same color as their mothers. Could it be that I had watched the birth of an albino bat, a pure-white bat without any pigment in its skin or fur?

As soon as the thought occurred to me I was sure that was the only explanation of what I had seen. I was certain the baby bat was an albino. A feeling of happiness came over me, a feeling of elation and fulfillment. Here was the solution of my problem of how to watch an individual bat. There would be no need for painting or banding or for marking a young bat in any way. Without any difficulty I could watch the bat I had just seen being born as it went through all the stages of its development, without confusing it with any of the others. It was the perfect solution to my problem, as though I had asked a question of the bats and they had given me the one absolute answer. It was a miracle.

That evening as I stood outside the grotto leaning against a tree (the rain had stopped, but the grass was still wet), I saw the bats swarm out into the open. For fifteen minutes I watched them hunting between the trees for insects and flying to the river for a drink. Then I saw her, the female I had seen giving birth. She flew by over my head, and as I looked up I saw a spot of pure white between her wings and I knew that the little albino baby was out for its first airing, its first taste and smell of the world. It could neither see nor hear as yet, for its eyes and ears were still closed, but it could probably feel the wind on its body and sense the fact that it was being whisked through space as it clung to its mother's fur.

VII

I WAS ANXIOUS TO TALK TO someone about what I had seen, and about albino bats in general. Was a pure-white albino bat considered a rarity, or were they as common as albino rats and mice? How much was known about them by scientists, and if they were common why had I never read anything about them, either in the book on bats or anywhere else? I knew of only one place where I could get such information, the Chicago Museum of Natural History, in Grant Park. I had visited the study section of the Museum a number of

times, and I was acquainted with a couple of young men
in the Department of Entomology, and also the Curator
of Birds. But I would have to talk to someone in Zoology
to get any information on bats, and in that department I
would be a stranger. So the very next day I went to the
museum, rode up to the third floor, and knocked on the
door marked Curator of Zoology.

There was no answer, so I opened the door and walked
in. There was no one in the room, and I stood for
ten minutes waiting for someone to arrive. There were
two desks in the room, and both of them were littered
with papers and books, and with the skulls and bones of
small animals. On a table in one corner stood jars of
various sizes, and I walked over to look at them. Each jar
contained some liquid (alcohol, I supposed) and an animal; there were frogs in some, snakes in others, and
birds and mice and moles. I saw one jar with a bat in it,
but it was not a little brown bat; it was about six inches
long and had a queer-shaped nose and large pointed ears.
It was hard to believe, looking at the bat in alcohol, that
it had ever been alive, that this sorry-looking mass of
skin and bones had ever flown through the air on those
folded black wings, or hung itself up on those tiny feet.

There was an open doorway leading to another room,
and after a time I saw a man come into the other room
and seat himself at a desk. I waited a few minutes more,

[78]

and then I went into the other room and stood beside the man, watching him. On the desk was a large bone that looked like the jaw of some animal, with two teeth in it, and he was drawing it on a large piece of white cardboard. I was sure he had noticed me, but he did not look up, and went on carefully drawing lines on the cardboard with a pen.

Finally, still without looking up, he said "How do you like it?"

"Fine," I said. "What is it supposed to be?"

"It's the lower jaw of a Himalayan black bear. Part of a project our Curator of Anatomy is working on."

"Is that so?"

"Yes, sir, been working on it for ten years now. When all the drawings are done, and all the comparative anatomy worked out, he'll publish a volume proving that the giant panda belongs somewhere between bears and raccoons. Scientists have never been sure, you know, of the exact relationship of the giant panda to other animals."

I studied the thought for a moment. "What made him decide to spend so many years on a project like that?"

"Well, you remember when Su-lin, the giant panda, died out at Brookfield Zoo about ten years ago? They gave us the carcass, and we've been studying it and drawing it and comparing it to other animals ever since. Eventually the Curator will get out a volume on the subject that will set the scientific world on its ears."

I did not know whether he was being sarcastic or not, so I said nothing. Did he hate sitting at a desk drawing the jaw of a bear, and did he resent the fact that when the Curator's volume finally appeared he would get no credit for the work he had done? How could I know what was going on in his mind? Finally, I asked him, "Do you know anything about little brown bats?"

"*Myotis lucifugus?* Sure, what do you want to know about them?"

"Well, for one thing, how common is a pure-white albino?"

He put his pen down, leaned back in his swivel chair, and looked up at me. He was a plump, heavy-set man with blond hair, and the lightest-blue eyes I had ever seen. "Don't tell me you know where we can get an albino specimen of *Myotis lucifugus!*"

I thought quickly, and decided to keep my secret to myself. "No," I said, "I just wondered how common they were."

"Well, three or four times since I've been with the Museum we've gotten reports that there was an albino bat in some part of the country, and we've sent men out to investigate. But we've never been able to authenticate the rumors, and we've never found a white bat. No one we've

things than that had been perpetrated in the name of science.

Later that afternoon I was back in the grotto, and as soon as I had entered, almost before my eyes became accustomed to the dim light, I saw the white bat. Though it was only a day old, it was already hanging from the roof of the grotto beside its mother, surrounded by some twenty other bats as though they were trying to hide it from prying eyes. But they could not possibly hide it, for the little white body hanging from the roof among the other bats was as conspicuous as a bright star shining in a dark firmament. I edged toward it slowly so as not to alarm the mother, and then closed my hand around the white body before the mother could fly off with it. Then, holding it in my hand and while its mother and a few of the other bats flew frenziedly around my head, I sat down on the floor of the grotto.

Holding the little bat in the palm of my hand I looked at it closely. First I determined that it was a female. Her eyes were still closed, and she wobbled when she tried to crawl, but she did not look like a spider, as the book had said these bats looked when they crawled. She looked like a little bride dressed in white, marching slowly and shakily down the aisle toward the altar, and her folded wings were like silken garments that she trailed along at her sides. She crawled out of my palm and onto my finger, sniffing as she went, and when she came to the end of my little finger she clamped her feet on it, swung herself over the edge of my hand, and hung there motionless. I put my head down and spoke to her in a whisper. "Little white lady," I said, "you are a rare thing, perhaps the only white bat in all the world. There are men who would give much to have you in a jar of alcohol, but you needn't worry, I will not give you away. You and I are going to be friends; I will observe you, and you will reveal to me some of the hidden bat secrets that no man has ever seen before."

Just as I finished speaking an amazing thing happened, a thing I would not have believed possible if I had not seen it. As I said before, a number of the bats were flying about in the grotto, and one of them would occasionally whiz past my head or zoom in front of my face. Suddenly one of them shot down to where the white lady was hanging from the tip of my little finger, there was a flutter of dark wings under my hand, and before I had time to realize what was happening they were both gone, the white baby bat and the other, which I presumed to be her mother. How had she accomplished this feat, how, without perching, almost without stopping, had she gotten her baby away from me? The whole action was performed so instantaneously that to my eyes it appeared she had plucked the baby bat off my finger in full flight

[84]

and yet I knew this was not so, for there had been no pull on my finger, no scraping of the baby's claws on the skin of my finger tip. In the tiny fraction of a second during which I had seen only a flutter of bat wings, the mother had probably stopped beside her baby and spread her tail membrane under it, the baby had let go her hold on my finger, and they had gone off together.

The whole action had occurred so quickly that I did not realize until it was over what had actually happened. But, I reflected, such an incident was probably not at all unusual to bats; the mother had found that there was plenty of time, in what was for me no time at all, to spread her tail membrane under her baby, perhaps even to wrap her wings around her, and for the little white bat to grasp her mother's fur with her thumbs, let go her hold on my finger, and go sailing off. It occurred to me that all the actions of these bats, their flight, their hunting, even their sleeping, seemed to me hurried and frantic, that they never did anything slowly or deliberately. The tempo of a bat's life was faster than mine, and since time is related to the tempo of one's living, then time moved faster for these bats than it did for me. Their time compared to mine like a swift-moving stream compared to a sluggish river, and if they had clocks the hands of their clocks would appear to me to be whirling madly around the face. But was it possible for me to see their clocks, could I, living as I did in my own slow tempo, peer out of my tempo into another time system, like an astronomer peering through a telescope at another universe? Could I ever get the "feel" of their lives, could I, a slow, languid, deliberate human being, know what it was like to be a quick, mercurial, agile bat? Perhaps, I thought, if I got to know them better, if I steeped myself in their lives, I could get an approximation of it. There would come a time when I would feel like one of them, and then perhaps I would perceive a faint glimmer of time rushing headlong past me, as it does for bats.

I do not remember what made me call her the white lady as I sat in the grotto holding her in my hand, but from that moment she was always the white lady to me. Afterward I read of an old legend about a ghostly, mysterious wraith that haunted a particular countryside in Germany, and was known to the inhabitants as the white lady. Of course this legend had no influence on my selection of the name for the albino bat, but it does seem like a curious coincidence that the name I bestowed upon a creature who always seemed to me a sort of mysterious, spectral little being, should also be associated with a legendary ghost.

VIII

UNTIL SHE WAS FIVE DAYS OLD
the white lady accompanied her mother wherever she
went, clinging to the fur on her stomach while her mother
hunted for insects outside the grotto and after she left at
nine thirty. Her days were spent hanging up beside her
mother on the roof, except when danger threatened (that
is, when I came too close to their perch). Then her mother
would whisk her off to go circling around the tree trunk.
When she was hungry she had only to squeak a few times
and stretch her head over to her left, where she knew her

mother was hanging, then her mother would take a step or two toward her, until the white lady could transfer her hold from the roof to her mother's fur, and she would climb on her mother's stomach and find her milk-laden breasts.

I now discovered that the bats had a strongly developed sense of position on the roof, amounting to a proprietary feeling toward their particular perch. Now, with the white lady to guide me, I could see how strongly each individual bat was attached to her particular perch. No matter what time I went into the grotto during the day, the white lady and her mother would be hanging in a particular spot on the roof, on the northeastern side of the grotto, about midway between the place where I entered and the tree trunk, where the roof was level with the top of my head. They were part of a compact cluster of bats, numbering twenty-six in all, which was separated from the nearest neighboring cluster by some two feet of blank roof. And not only were these twenty-six bats at home in this particular spot on the roof of the grotto, but each bat had its own particular position in the group. The white lady always hung from a certain vine stem, with her mother on her left and the other bats grouped somewhat as in this diagram, where W is the white lady, M her mother, and O's the other bats.

```
        O O O O
   OOO  W  M  OO
      O O O O O O
   O O O O O
     O O O O
```

I do not mean to imply that the white lady and her
mother never hung themselves up anywhere else in the
grotto. When the bats were nervous or excited they would
fly around the tree trunk, and when they finally perched
it might not be in their habitual spot. This was especially
true after I had come into the grotto and begun prowling
about, before I settled down. When I came to within
three or four feet of the group that included the white
lady, each mother in the group (eleven of the twenty-
six were babies) clasped her offspring to herself with
one wing, and then the whole group flew off to circle
about the trunk. If it was morning, the white lady's
mother would circle the tree for only a minute or two,
and then hang herself up somewhere, usually on the side
of the grotto opposite to where I happened to be at the
time. If it was afternoon she might fly about in the grotto
for as long as twenty minutes before perching; but if it
was evening, and many of the bats were circling the tree
trunk preparatory to going out, she would join them and
continue on the wing until it was time to leave the grotto.

But, whether it was morning or afternoon, and wherever the white lady and her mother happened to perch after I had disturbed them, if I sat down on the floor of the grotto and did not move for ten minutes, there began a constant changing of position among the bats, and soon the white lady was hanging beside her mother in their accustomed place, with the twenty-four other bats in their regular positions in the group. This occurred even when I was sitting with my head less than three feet from where they hung, directly under the group. They seemed to have no fear of me when I sat quietly on the floor; it was only when I was moving toward them that they became nervous.

Now a peculiar thing about these changes of position was the fact that a bat was not welcome in any group but her own; for some reason they seemed to be suspicious of any stranger to their group, and to try to chase her away. When a bat hung herself up among a group of which she was not a member the other bats all turned their heads toward her, bared their sharp little teeth, and squeaked menacingly. Even if she belonged in the group but was not in her rightful position, the others went through the motions of trying to chase her away. But if she was a stranger from another group the mothers among them would, if she continued to hang there despite their threats, clasp their babies to them with one wing

[90]

as though to protect them, and sometimes even fly away with their young. If the stranger was herself a mother, and hung her baby up beside her among the group, the others would relax somewhat, they would take their wings from about their own babies and even urge the young to leave their fur, though they would continue to bare their teeth and squeak at the strange pair.

In view of the fact that there are among the bats at this period some females who, for whatever reason, are childless, it seems to me at least possible that the mothers are in constant fear of having their young kidnaped by these childless females. It would be perfectly natural for some mother who had lost her own child to try to take one from another female, and this would explain the reaction of the mothers in a group to strangers. But if this were true the mothers would be suspicious of any childless female, and this is not the case when the female belongs to their own group. There were four females without children in the group to which the white lady belonged, and I never noticed that the others treated them any differently than they did the mothers, or were the least bit suspicious of them.

On the fifth day of the white lady's existence her eyes opened, and a new sense was added to those with which she perceived the world. I have read that sight is not very important to a bat, that they depend more for the per-

[91]

ception of their environment on the senses of hearing and smell, since most of their active life is spent in darkness anyway. While I cannot absolutely disprove this statement, I have reason to believe it is not true. I believe bats are as dependent on sight as are, say, owls, which are also active during the hours of darkness. And if the hearing of bats is more acute than that of some other animals (and even this is open to question), there is no reason for believing that their sight is correspondingly weaker. A dog, say a bloodhound, has a much keener sense of smell than a man, but there is no evidence to show that dogs are less dependent on their sense of sight than are men; as a matter of fact, a sightless bloodhound is a much more helpless creature than a blind man.

When a human baby opens its eyes for the first time, there is a long period when the child is still unable to co-ordinate what it sees, when it can distinguish little more than differences in light intensity. This was not the case with the white lady. On the evening of the day her eyes opened she could see perfectly, though I do not suppose her eyesight was as keen as that of an adult bat. She saw me when I came toward her that evening as she hung alone from the roof of the grotto, and she quickly climbed up and tried to hide herself in the vegetation. Later I watched her playing with the other young bats as though she had been seeing them all her life.

[92]

On the evening of that day her mother left her in the grotto when she went out hunting, and never again did she go out clinging to her mother's fur. She was to remain in the grotto now until she could leave it on her own wings. I am not positive that there is any connection between the opening of her eyes and the being left in the grotto all night, but it seems more than a mere coincidence. Before her eyes were open she was a helpless little creature, which could only hang motionless from the roof, and when she thought she was in danger, as when a large human hand closed about her, she could do nothing but squeak for her mother. Now she could see danger approaching, and hide from it in the vegetation. Before her eyes were open there would have been nothing to do all night long in the grotto; now she could move about and investigate the various parts of it, and she could play with the other young bats who, like herself, had been left there by their mothers.

As in the case of other animals, the play of young bats evolves gradually as they mature. However, in the case of most other animals there is almost always more than one baby in a litter, and the tendency to play with its brothers and sisters is natural almost from birth. But bats are born singly, they have no brothers or sisters, and as far as I could observe there is no play activity until the young are old enough to be left alone in the grotto

[93]

all night. This may or may not be due to the fact that until that time their eyes are not yet open. At any rate, two young bats hanging side by side from the roof never show any interest in each other, or any impulse to play, until they are about a week old.

On the first few nights that the white lady was left in the grotto by her mother, she hung for an hour or so after her mother left from the roof. Then she crawled up among the vegetation and went exploring. In and out among the stems and leaves she climbed, sniffing here and there as she went, sometimes falling to the floor, then crawling to where the vegetation met the ground and climbing up again. In her wanderings among the vegetation she often met another young bat about her own age (all the young bats were about her age, since they are all born within a few days of each other), also bent on exploring. They would raise their heads to look at each other through their newly opened eyes, sniff each other carefully here and there, and then go on their separate ways. If the bat she met was a few days older than she, he might bare his teeth at her playfully and squeak, but she was not yet ready for play, and she would back away from him hurriedly.

After a few days of this sort of random exploratory activity she began to spend more of her time with the other young bats she met among the vegetation. At first

[94]

it was usually she and one other bat who would play together, but occasionally a third would join them. They would scramble about among the vines and creepers, chasing or being chased, biting each other playfully, squeaking the high, nasal squeak of very young bats. Once I saw her threading her way through the vegetation with her jaws firmly clamped on the hind leg of another young bat who was crawling in front of her, and she did not let go her hold until both fell to the floor. Their play at this period of their childhood seemed to consist entirely of chasing and biting each other, and squeaking.

Gradually, as she became older, her play activity became more complex, and she became involved in relationships with more and more of the other young bats. I would often see her among a group of forty or more young bats, all of whom were squeaking and biting and crawling over and under each other in what appeared to me to be some elaborate game, the rules of which I could not possibly understand. Sometimes early in the evening, just after their mothers had left, a few of the bats would engage in a game that always reminded me of a jousting tournament. Still hanging from the roof where their mothers had left them, two young bats would edge toward each other, baring their teeth and squeaking as they came close. When their bodies were touching they began beating their wings at each other, biting and pushing with

[95]

their heads. Soon other bats in the vicinity would come up to join the melee, and before long there would be twenty or more of them all beating their wings and pushing and biting and squeaking. Eventually some would fall to the floor and others would crawl up away from the battle, until only one was left, and he would bare his teeth and squeak and turn all about, like a young boy with his fists up daring anyone to come over and fight.

In all this play in the grotto, in all the activity with the other bats engaged in by the white lady, I never saw any indication that the others were prejudiced against her because she was different from themselves, or that they regarded her as either inferior or superior. I realize that this is a somewhat ridiculous statement to make, since I could not possibly know what the other bats thought of her. Still, in their actions they seemed to me to regard her as one of themselves who happened to be born with white skin and fur.

One evening when the white lady was eleven days old I was sitting on the grass just outside the grotto watching the adult bats hunting for insects among the trees. It was after eight o'clock, and though the sun had set a few small clouds in the western sky still glowed a deep, dark red, like the embers of a dead fire. Suddenly my eyes were attracted to a movement of something white on the roof of the grotto, and turning my

head I saw the white lady emerging above the top of the
vegetation. She had probably been crawling about among
the leaves and vines, and had found her way out. Whether
this happened frequently or not I do not know, but because the idea appealed to me I preferred to think of it
as being the first time. And the way she acted on the roof
of the grotto, it did seem to be the first time. She stood up
as high as she could on her legs and wrists and sniffed
the air. I could imagine her thinking she had never
smelled anything so fragrant as the odor of grasses and
clover and milkweed and dandelion, brought to her on a
warm breeze that also carried the smell of the water in
the river. Then she turned her head slowly from side to
side, and it seemed to me that she was drinking in the
sounds that filled the air, the soft swish of the breeze
among the trees, the chirping of crickets and rasping of
katydids, the blowing of an auto horn on California
Avenue, perhaps some sound that I could not hear uttered
by the flying bats, maybe even the death cries of the
insects they were catching. Finally she looked up, out
past the branches of the locust tree and into the air where
her mother and the other adult bats were wheeling and
diving and zooming about. For fully five minutes she
stood up on her legs and wrists, staring as though she
were entranced at the bats flying about.

What thoughts were going through that little white

head of hers, I wondered, what dreams and hopes and aspirations? Perhaps this was the first time she had ever seen creatures like herself flying through the outdoor air, and her mind must be filled with wonder and awe at the beauty of their flight. Did she realize that in just a few weeks she, too, would be out here every evening, skimming along and diving down and zooming up, chasing the insects that flew up from the grass, and dipping her tongue in the river to get a drink? How marvelous it must seem to her to have fingers encased in skin, and to have only to wave them gently to be wafted upward toward the sky.

IX

IT WAS AT THIS PERIOD THAT I
began taking the white lady home with me. When I arrived at the grotto early in the evening, just after the adults had left, I would usually see her hanging from her accustomed perch. If she was not there I knew she was crawling about among the vegetation, and I had only to stand in one spot and look sharply all about on the roof, and eventually I would see a little white body crawling among the dark leaves. When she saw me coming toward her she would hurry to get away, but, unless she was on

a part of the roof that was high over my head, I never had any trouble finding her. If she was on the roof out of my reach I might have to climb up one of the branches of the locust tree to get her, but this was not too difficult a feat.

When my hand came close to her, and she saw that her capture was imminent, she always turned to face my fingers, bared her teeth at them like an angry little dog, and squeaked. Then I would bring the tips of my fingers slowly up to her face, and hold them there while she sniffed them. After that she would close her mouth and stop squeaking, and I could pick her up without danger of being bitten. I am certain that she was familiar with the smell of my fingers, for I had been picking her up and holding her in my hand since she was two days old. But was she afraid, when she bared her teeth and squeaked, that it was not the familiar I, but some other human being who had come to try to capture her? And if it had been someone else, if the smell of the fingers was unfamiliar, would she have bitten him? I cannot answer these questions, for as far as I know there has never been any other person in the grotto, and no one but me has ever tried to pick her up. But even though she has never smelled the fingers of any other human being, we had to go through the formality of recognition each time before she would allow herself to be picked up.

[100]

I had fixed up a wooden cigar box to carry her in, with air holes in the top and a clasp on the lid so she could not get out. When I arrived home I would transfer her from the cigar box to a small canary cage, around which I had put screen wire, for she could easily have squeezed between the bars of the cage. But despite the screen wire, and despite my continual efforts to stop up every opening through which she could escape, she often managed during the night to get out, and I would come to her cage in the morning and find it empty. Then I would have to search the house for her, looking everywhere, on the floor, the walls, the ceiling, behind radiators and stoves and pictures and bookcases, under tables and chairs, in every corner and under every molding in the house. Whereas in the grotto the whiteness of her skin and fur made her conspicuous, in our home it had the opposite effect, and she was harder to find than if she had been dark brown. If she was motionless on the white curtains in our kitchen, or hanging from the white ceiling in our living room, she was practically invisible, and I could not find her until she made some movement.

My mother, poor thing, hated the sight of her. She took one look at her the first time I brought her home, shuddered as though she had seen the devil, and never looked at her again. On the mornings when the white lady had gotten out of her cage my mother lay shivering in her bed until I found her and put her back in the cage. She had a horrible, nameless fear of the little bat, and nothing I could say to her succeeded in calming her fears. I tried to reason with her, I used every form of logical argument, and I worked on her sympathy, but I might as well have been trying to sell the devil to a devout churchman.

"Mother," I would say to her as I brought the white lady into the living room on my palm, "just look at her for a minute. Isn't she beautiful?"

"Take her away," my mother would scream as she averted her head, "take that awful thing away from here, I hate her."

"But, mother, she's only a little baby. How can you hate such a harmless, innocent young creature?"

"She's evil, that's why I hate her. All those bats you spend so much time with are evil, they're horrible, loathsome, repulsive things, and I won't have anything to do with them. I don't even want to see them."

"Now listen, mother. You're a sensible person, and I want to talk to you sensibly. Why do you hate these bats? Surely you don't believe all those old wives' tales about bats visiting graveyards and hobnobbing with ghosts. You can't seriously believe that these tiny mammals suck the blood of sleeping children, or that they try to get tangled up in people's hair. They're just little

[102]

animals, like field mice or squirrels, and they live out their lives in a perfectly natural way, without bothering people or being bothered by them. Because they happen to have wings, they fly, and because their ancestors for millions of years have been nocturnal, they fly about at night. But why should you think they're evil, or that there's anything repulsive or unclean about them?"

"My darling, you're such a logical person, maybe you really *should* have been a scientist. But there are things that even a scientist can't understand, things that one feels. Don't ask me to explain why I hate your bats, because I don't know myself. I only know that when I think of them I have a presentiment of evil. I tell you, darling, something horrible is going to happen to you some night under that tree."

Though I made light of her fears, and tried to show her how silly it was to believe the bats could harm me in any way, I knew that she was sincere, and that she really did worry about me when she knew I was in the grotto. But it never occurred to me to stop going to the grotto, or not to spend a night now and then under the tree, and there was no chance now that I would forsake the white lady because of the foolish fears of my mother. What could possibly happen to me? I was as safe in the grotto as I was in my own home, and what was more important, I was happier.

When I first transferred the white lady from the cigar box to the cage, she would crawl about on the bottom for a few minutes, sniffing here and there at the screen wire and at the newspaper I had laid down. Then, using her thumbs and her feet, she would climb up the side of the cage onto the roof, and hang herself up by her feet from a particular spot on the roof. It did not make any difference which way the cage was turned, or whether her corner was brightly lighted or in the shade, she invariably went to her favorite perch to hang herself up. For about half an hour she hung there, as though I had interrupted her rest when I picked her up in the grotto and she was determined to finish it out. But she did not sleep, her eyes remained open and were focused on me if I was in the room, and if I moved about I could see her head turn to follow me.

After she had had enough rest she began crawling about in the cage, up one side, across the roof, and down the other, sniffing in every corner, trying every slight opening to see if she could squeeze through. This activity went on all evening long, while I watched her; and I suppose it went on during the night too, when I was asleep and the house was in total darkness. And it quite often happened that during the night she found some opening that could be spread enough to admit her body, and so she would escape and go prowling around in the dark-

[104]

ness. How she managed to get out I could never discover; there was not an opening in the cage with a diameter greater than a quarter of an inch, and she was almost full grown now, measuring an inch and a half from the tip of her ears to her feet. But however she managed it, she did frequently get out, and when she did I think she prowled around in the darkness for the rest of the night, for in the morning often I found her far away from the cage.

Sometimes in the evening while I sat beside the cage watching her, she hung herself up from the roof of the cage and cleaned herself. This was an interesting performance, and I was always delighted when I saw her begin it. First, with her bright pink tongue, she licked the parts of her body she could reach, the fur on her stomach and sides, her tail membrane and feet and wings. Then, like a cat cleaning its face, she licked her thumb and rubbed it over her head and her eyes and nose and ears. Then she cleaned the inside of her ears, licking each thumb half a dozen times to clean the ear on that side, and when she was through with each ear she shook her thumb about in it, like a man who has gotten soap in his ear. Finally she let go her hold on the roof with one foot and began combing her fur with her toes, running through the white fur with quick, lightninglike strokes of her feet, bringing her head up so that she could comb it, twisting her body about so that she could reach her back and side,

[105]

and then changing feet to comb the other side of her body. From beginning to end her cleaning took about fifteen minutes.

Where had she learned to perform such an elaborate toilet, I wondered. Was it a purely instinctive process, or had she watched her mother go through the same actions? And if she had watched her mother, why was it necessary for an adult bat, which almost never touched the ground, to clean herself so thoroughly? Could it be that bats were cleaner than other animals, that they were more fastidious about cleanliness? When I thought about it, I could not remember ever having seen a bat, either the white lady or another, with dirt on her fur or her body, or with her fur matted, as so often happens with a dog or cat. And the musky smell that pervaded the grotto came, I had discovered, not from the bats themselves, but from their droppings. When I held the white lady to my nose she smelled as fresh and clean as a newly bathed baby.

I often tried to feed her various things, insects and fruit and even milk, but without success. She never ate anything I offered her at this period. I would tear the wings off a fly and hold it in front of her face, but she paid no attention. If I opened her mouth and put the fly in, she immediately pushed it out again with her tongue. A few times I dipped a little cloth in milk and put it in her mouth, but when she closed her jaws and got a taste

[106]

of the milk she spit it out violently and backed away from the cloth. Neither did I ever see her drink any water, though I kept a little pan of it in her cage.

There was one night when it seemed to me she was beginning to show an interest in insects, like the first awakening of a taste for what later would be her only food. She was eighteen days old at the time, and I had pulled the wings off a fly and offered it to her. When she backed away from it I dropped it in her cage, where it walked about over the paper. For a time she stood on her feet and her wrists eyeing the fly, turning her head to follow its movements, and then she began moving toward it, following it about, crouching low on her wrists like a cat stalking a mouse. Finally she pounced on it and took it in her mouth; then, sitting down like a little bear, she brought her head down to her tail membrane and began playing with the fly there. I have read that it is characteristic of adult bats to use the tail membrane while in the air as a sort of temporary pocket to hold an insect while they turn it about and get a good grip on it. But she soon tired of this and began crawling away, and when the fly dropped to the floor of the cage I saw that she had not even bitten it. It was alive and walking.

When I took the white lady home with me at night, I always brought her back to the grotto the next morning, on my way downtown. This was usually about nine o'clock, a number of hours after the adult bats had returned, and the grotto was quiet and peaceful, the occupants hanging from the roof, either resting or asleep. Most of the young bats had already suckled their fill and were hanging beside their mothers. The white lady's mother was in her usual place on the roof, and beside her was an empty space where her daughter belonged. After the first flutter at my entrance, there was not a movement in the grotto, nor any sound to break the stillness.

I would sit down on the floor at the opposite end of the grotto from where the white lady's mother hung, put the cigar box down, and open the lid. The minute the lid was off the white lady would rear up on her feet and sniff the air, and, knowing that she was home, she would utter a little squeak. It was such a faint squeak, so nearly inaudible, that I, whose ears were directly above her, could just barely hear it amidst the silence. But to her mother it was a clarion call, it was the voice of her daughter come home at last. When I opened the lid I would keep my eyes on the spot where the white lady's mother hung, and the instant the squeak broke the stillness I would see her leave her perch and go circling around the tree trunk. None of the other bats moved. If they heard the squeak at all they doubtless considered it a sound private to the white lady and her mother, which did not concern them.

After circling the grotto two or three times, and perhaps hearing the white lady squeak again, her mother would swoop down to where she stood in the cigar box and pick her up. But the statement "pick her up" is so inadequate to explain what took place, and gives no idea of the lightninglike complexity of the action, nor of the white lady's part in it. It was an instantaneous transfer of the white lady from the box to the fur on her mother's stomach, and it occurred so quickly that no matter how intently I might strain my eyes to see, nor how close to the white lady I might bend my head, it always appeared to me as it did the first time I saw it happen; there was a sudden blur of dark wings over the box—the mother was flying off and the white lady had disappeared. I knew how it happened, and I knew too that the only reason I could not see the actual transfer taking place was that it occurred too quickly, and yet I could not rid my mind of the feeling each time that something uncanny and miraculous had just taken place: that a little white bat had disappeared before my eyes.

X

I LIKE TO THINK THAT JUNE 20 was a red-letter day on the white lady's calendar, a day to remember and to celebrate each year. For on that date, when she had reached the age of twenty-three days, she flew for the first time. But perhaps I, like some fond mother waiting for her child to take his first step, am exaggerating the importance of this event; perhaps to her the act of flying was a perfectly natural result of previous attempts to stay in the air. It must have seemed important to her at the time, but whether it remained important after she had been flying a few days, and whether she remembered her first flight in the weeks that followed, I do not know. A child's first step is important too, but who, after he has become an adult, remembers the date on which he walked for the first time?

I am not even certain that I witnessed her first flight, but that is a technical matter which does not seem very important to me. As far as I know, and therefore as far as I am concerned, the first time I saw her fly was her first flight. For all I know there may have been preliminary attempts, with awkward flapping of wings and falling to the ground; but I did not see any of these attempts, and my first sight of the white lady in flight was a vision of perfect control and balance, of perfect co-ordination of wings and tail membrane and body. This is so different from the first flight of young birds, which I have watched many times, that it is worth discussing. The span of life of most small birds is about the same as that of these bats, from four to six years. The young are born as helpless, and they learn to fly at about the same age, when they are three or four weeks old. But even after a young bird has left the nest and fluttered to the ground, it would hardly be accurate to say he can fly. He can flap his wings mightily and, by running full speed along the ground, rise two or three feet upward. It is not until a

[112]

week or more after they have left the nest that most young birds can rise more than a few feet into the air.

But when a young bat launches himself into the air for the first time he has already mastered the technique of flight, he is already capable of catching a few flying insects and of remaining in the air for at least a few hours. Not only is it not necessary for his parents to teach him to fly, but there is also no necessity for a long period of training and practice; as soon as a young bat can fly he is already an accomplished aerialist.

On June 20 I came into the grotto late in the evening, while the adults were outside hunting insects, intending to take the white lady home with me. I had not seen her the day before, for I had not come to the grotto at all. My mother had been ill, and when I got home from the office in the afternoon she was lying in bed, tossing about and groaning. But she refused to let me call a doctor, or even take her temperature. "What's the use of calling a doctor, darling, I know what he'll say. He'll say it's all due to nervousness, and I know that myself. If only I wasn't alone so much, there would be nothing wrong with me. Promise me that you'll stay home tonight, and I'll be all right again. The only medicine I need is the comfort of your presence."

So for the first time in more than two weeks I had not gone to the grotto, either to watch the bats or to bring the white lady home. Less than five minutes after I entered the grotto on the following day, I was sorry I had given in to my mother's possessive neurosis. For the day I had chosen to stay home was an important one in the development of the white lady from a baby to an adult bat, and who could tell what I had missed? It was on that day that she must have tried to fly for the first time. Had she succeeded on the first attempt, or did it take trial after trial before her wings were able to keep her aloft? Was the first attempt an accident, had she been pushed from her perch on the roof by one of the other young bats, and while falling beaten her wings, and found that she could fly? Or had her first attempts to fly been deliberate, had she let go her hold on the roof and beaten her wings to see if they were ready to carry her?

She was not the first of the young bats to learn to fly. For the past week, whenever I came into the grotto late in the evening, a few of the bats hanging from the roof would launch themselves out when I came close to them in my search for the white lady, and circle the tree trunk a few times before finding another perch. These were undoubtedly young bats which had just learned to fly, for if they had been adults they would be outside with the others hunting insects. But since, except for the white lady, I could not identify any individuals in the grotto, I was never sure either how old these bats were, or when they had first learned to fly. I guessed that they were probably a few days or a week older than the white lady, and that they had flown for the first time on the day I saw them circle the tree trunk.

Having seen a number of the other young bats flying for a week past, I suppose I should have anticipated this normal stage in her development. But I was not prepared for it, and when it happened it came as a complete surprise to me. In a way I was like a mother overcome with emotion on seeing her child take his first step, even though she knows that other children his age in the neighborhood have been walking for weeks. Yet I suppose in another way I had somewhat the feeling of a father who looks at his little girl and for the first time realizes that she is a woman. I was more surprised by the revolution her flight was causing in my conception of her than by the flight itself. For in that instant when for the first time I saw her launch herself into the air, she ceased to be the helpless, crawling, dependent little being I had known for twenty-three days, and became a mature, self-sufficient, beautiful female bat.

When I entered the grotto that evening the white lady was hanging from the roof in her usual place. I walked toward her, anticipating that she would crawl up among the vegetation when I came close. But she continued to hang there until I stood beside her, my face only a few inches from her body. I stood looking at her for a second, wondering if something were wrong, and then I put my hand up to get her. Later it occurred to me that she had deliberately allowed me to come closer than usual, had let my hand come to within a few inches of her body, to heighten my surprise at seeing her fly away from me for the first time. Just as I was about to close my hand around her she let go her hold on the roof and launched herself out in the grotto, her white wings flashing through the dimness as she flew around and around the tree trunk. Twice her wings brushed against my face as I stood there filled with amazement, as though she wanted to be sure I was paying attention to her, like a child who cries "Look at me, look what I can do." Finally, after five or six circuits of the tree trunk, she hung herself up at the other side of the grotto, and I sat down on the floor to ponder this new development.

So, I thought, that was the end of the baby bat I had so often held in my hand, that had crawled about in my home, and hidden from me among the vegetation of the roof. Now she was an adult, and I would have to learn to know her all over again, to observe her adult habits and her grown-up ways. She would no longer be confined to the grotto, but be flying about outdoors every evening, and every night go with the other bats wherever they went after nine thirty. Suppose someone saw her as she flew about outside the grotto hunting insects—and who in the neighborhood could miss a pure white bat flying in the twilight? It would not be long after someone saw her that a man would come with a gun, intent on destroying her life so as to preserve her body, and that would be the end, not only of the white lady, but probably of the other bats in the grotto too, and of my observations of them. This new development boded no good either for the white lady or for me, and I sat on the grotto floor plunged in gloom.

Then the white lady launched herself into the air again, circling around and around the grotto, and every time she came to where I sat she dipped low as though to call attention to herself, sometimes brushing her wings lightly against my face. As I watched her going around, her body making a circular blur of white that wove through the dim light of the grotto, I could feel the gloom and the sadness leaving my mind, to be replaced by an anticipation of the pleasure I would have in watching her flying about outside, catching insects, and taking a drink in the river and gliding down and zooming upward. What a fool I had been to worry about what might happen to the white lady now that she could fly.

I stayed in the grotto for about two hours that evening, watching the white lady launch herself again and again into the air to exercise her wings, and try her new-found skill. Before I left it was pitch dark, but still I could dimly see her white form circling the tree trunk, like a faintly luminous particle whirling around in some dark medium. I did not take her home with me that night, though I suppose I could have caught her with the butter-fly net I kept in the grotto. But I did not have the heart to confine her, first in a cigar box and then in a cage at home, on this, her first night of flight. Let her be free tonight, I said to myself; whatever happens afterward, let her have this one night to glory in her ability to fly.

The next evening I went to the grotto again, but this time earlier, before the adults had gone out for their night's hunting. Most of the bats were whirling around the tree trunk when I came in, and whirling around with them was the white lady, as conspicuous in the blur of dark wings circling the grotto as a white rose in a field of cabbages. I was almost certain, when I saw her with the others, that tonight she would go out to hunt with the adults, and so I went outside and sat down in the grass at a little distance from the grotto to await their exit.

When they came out there was the usual sudden smokelike eruption from the top of the grotto. I thought I caught a quick glimpse of a white speck in the dark eruption, like a brightly burning cinder in the black smoke, but I could not be sure of this. It was not until the "smoke" spread out and resolved itself into myriads of

[118]

little winged bats that I saw her plainly. She was zooming and diving and zigzagging this way and that with the other bats, and she seemed as much at home in the air as any of the others. One would never have guessed that this was the first time she had ever left the grotto on her own wings. I do not know whether or not she was catching insects, though she may very well have been hunting, for a few days previously she had begun to show an interest in insects, as I have explained before. But I know she was not yet completely weaned from her mother's breast, because two days later I saw her clinging to the fur on her mother's stomach, with the older bat trying to hide with her wing the white body that was almost as big as her own.

For two hours I sat outside the grotto watching the white lady flying about in the air with the other bats, and a thought kept running through my head: How beautiful, how beautiful she is. She was so light, so graceful, so airy and insubstantial; she was like some divine little being who had come down to dance above the earth, and I felt as I watched her that at any minute she might leave the company of the dark little flying mice and ascend to her ethereal castle. Diving through the air and skimming over my head, it seemed to me that she was like the materialization of some vision I might have had, the embodiment of a dream of pure beauty.

[119]

As the sun slowly sank over the rim of the earth the whiteness of her body changed to rosy pink, and from her wings there flashed, every now and then as she tilted them, a shaft of orange light reflected from the sun. Even after the sun was gone and the air outside the grotto darkened, she still retained some of the pink and orange light bequeathed her by the sun, and she flashed across the sky like a comet, weaving back and forth. And then suddenly it was time for them to leave. The white lady and the other bats disappeared as though a magician had waved his wand, and not a bat was left in the air. I was abandoned in the darkness, and for a time I continued sitting in the grass outside the grotto remembering the beauty of what I had just seen, as one sometimes sits in a theater after the curtain has descended on a thrilling play. Then I got up and walked to California Avenue, and when I saw the cars passing and the people walking down the street, my fears returned to me. How many more nights would I be able to watch the white lady flying about outside the grotto before someone else saw her, and came to get her? There was no doubt in my mind that her days were numbered.

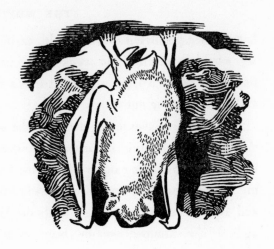

XI

FROM THAT DAY ON I BEGAN
going to the grotto every evening, not only to watch the
white lady fly, but to be sure that she was still there.
Driving to California Avenue, and walking across the
field toward the grotto, I would be filled with a heavy
feeling of apprehension. I always knew that no one but
me had seen her before nine thirty the night before, but
how did I know what might have happened to her after
she left the vicinity of the grotto? Where did she go, and
what dangers was she exposed to there? If it was evening,

I would see her flying over the field, or if it was earlier she would be circling the trunk in the grotto, and the feeling of apprehension would lift like a fog dispelled, and my heart sang out with joy.

If, when I walked across the field, the bats were outside the grotto hunting for insects the white lady would welcome me by diving down toward me from high over my head, flashing her wings a few inches from my face, and lightly brushing my hair with the fur under her body as she skimmed over my head. None of the other bats ever took such liberties with me, and I have often wondered whether the white lady would have been as friendly to someone else walking across the field. The thought has once or twice crossed my mind, that I might bring some trusted friend along and have him walk across the field to see if the white lady went through her usual ceremony of welcome with him. But I never did this, for there was always the element of danger in sharing my secret with someone, and besides I would feel too much like the foolish husband who brings a friend home to see if his wife will flirt with him.

One evening, standing outside the grotto while the bats flew about overhead, I saw on the ground at my feet a small grasshopper hopping about grotesquely, as though something were the matter with him. I picked him up to examine him, and found that he had only one hind

[122]

leg, and could not hop very well. I let him stand on the palm of my open hand, and while I waited for him to hop away I idly wondered how he had come to lose a leg. Perhaps he had been in a fight with another grasshopper, or maybe a female had chewed his leg off while they were copulating. Or had he been captured by a snake or a frog, and sacrificed a leg for freedom?

Suddenly a white body dived downward toward my hand. There was a blur of white wings above my palm, and the grasshopper disappeared. The white lady had taken the grasshopper from my hand, just as her mother used to snatch her away from me when she was still a baby. I searched about in the grass until I found another insect. It was a brown beetle, about a third the size of the grasshopper, and as I watched it crawling over my outstretched palm I wondered if she would be able to see it from high in the air. I kept my eyes on her as she flew about overhead, and I saw her swoop down toward me like a dive bomber toward its target. Again there was a white blur of wings just above my hand, and when it was gone the beetle had disappeared and the white lady was zooming upward. I fed her four more insects in this manner, and then it was time for the bats to leave. The last one she took from my hand was a tiny ladybird, and by this time it was so dark that I could not see the insect myself as it crawled over my hand. But though flying

twenty feet above me, she saw it and swooping unerr-
ingly picked it up without touching my hand.

After that evening I fed her insects every time I came
to the grotto. She accepted everything that was alive on
my palm, though I have no way of knowing whether she
ate all the insects she took from me. Oddly enough, she
would not take a dead insect, and sometimes when an
insect was motionless on my palm she would skin over
my hand without picking it up, evidently believing it to
be dead. I suppose some of the insects she took from me
were distasteful to her, but she never showed by her
actions that she was displeased with anything I offered
her, and I suppose she reasoned that it was easy enough
to spit out anything she disliked. As a matter of fact,
there were plenty of insects in the air, so I do not believe
that necessity played any part in her acceptance of food
from me. If she had been hungry the other bats would
have been hungry too, and they would have followed her
lead in taking insects from my hand. But none of the
other bats paid any attention to me except when I disturbed them as they hung from the roof of the grotto;
they never swooped to welcome me as I walked across
the field, or took insects from my hand. And so I can
only presume that when the white lady accepted food
from my hand, the action meant more to her than a mere
addition to her diet, just as it meant more to me than

[124]

merely feeding her as I might feed a squirrel or a pigeon. It was, I think, a token of our friendship, a symbol of our regard for each other, and a demonstration that a man and bat could be friends in spite of all the differences between them, in spite of the fact that they lived on totally dissimilar planes of existence.

One evening I went to the grotto early, for I was going to try to catch the white lady in my net and bring her home with me. I was anxious to take some photographs of her in various positions; in flight, hanging up by her feet, and crawling on the floor, and the only way I could do this was in my home where I had the equipment. The bats were circling the tree trunk when I arrived, and I got the net and stood in the center of the grotto waiting. Every time I saw the white lady approaching I pushed the net up in front of her, but each time she managed to swerve aside in time to avoid being captured. Sometimes I caught two or three bats, but when I saw that the white lady was not in the net I released them. Finally, after about twenty minutes, I caught her in the net, then took her out and put her in the cigar box.

At home, before I opened the cigar box, I closed all the windows, then got my camera and other equipment ready. There was an electric fan going in the living room, and if I had been more careful I would have turned this off before releasing the white lady; but for some reason I neglected to do this. It was a new fan that I had bought for my mother, a floor model with an eighteen-inch blade, and two speeds. On hot days my mother kept it going constantly at the slower speed, though why she had it going on that particular day, with the temperature in the sixties, I do not know. As usual, my mother had locked herself in her room when she knew I was bringing the white lady home, and would not come out until the bat was gone.

When I opened the cigar box the white lady flew up immediately and began circling the living room just under the ceiling. Then she flew into the dining room, circled that a few times as though she wanted to familiar-ize herself with all the rooms in this strange house, then into the kitchen, and back to the living room. I picked up the camera, adjusted it and put a flash bulb into the socket, and stood in the center of the living room waiting until she should come down to within range. As she flew about just under the ceiling she suddenly perceived the fan standing on the floor beside the couch, and flew directly toward it. Powerless to do anything in that split second, I could only stand there aghast and watch her dive toward the revolving blade, then zoom up over the top of it. I took one step toward it, intending to turn it off, but before I could reach it she was back again, diving

[126]

toward the fan, and this time she went headlong into it, between the metal guards and into the whirling blade.

For an instant I was stunned by what I had just witnessed, for it seemed to me that she had deliberately committed suicide. For a fraction of a second I stood motionless with the camera in my hand, too horrified to move, and there welled up within me a whole sequence of images, like the review of one's life that is supposed to rush through the mind just before death. I saw the white lady being born again, dropping into her mother's tail membrane while she was still attached to the umbilical cord; I felt her crawling over my hand, sniffing at my fingers with her queer-shaped little nose, and hanging herself up from the end of my little finger; I watched her fly for the first time, in the grotto and then outside of it; and I saw the white blur of her wings above my outstretched hand as she took the insect I was offering her. Mixed with these images, an integral part of them now, was grief at her death, and remorse that I had been the cause of it.

I have often wondered since then how much time elapsed while these images, dragging their attendant emotions, were going through my mind. It would be interesting to know how long it takes a single image or thought to flash up into consciousness and then move off to make room for another. Can it be that thoughts and images observe a time sense different from that shown by our clocks and watches, or that they move faster than the speed of light and are therefore outside of time altogether? It must be something like that, for otherwise how could all the images and emotions I have enumerated have taken place between the moment I saw the white lady enter the fan, and the moment I saw her flying upward from behind it? For she was not killed, she was not even touched by the blade. She had flown into the fan and come out the other side as easily as a child jumping a rope. Now, in my relief at seeing her again, I could smile at my groundless feelings of grief and remorse. Suicide, indeed—she had known exactly what she was doing.

After that first dash into the fan, she came back and did it again and again, glorying in her ability to fly through the whirling blade, deliberately showing off her skill to me, her audience. I suppose she sensed my admiration for her daring and her swiftness and skill in avoiding the blade, for she kept rushing through the fan, like a child turning somersaults for admiring parents. After I had watched her go through the fan more than a dozen times I decided to try an experiment. I walked to the fan and turned it to the higher speed. She dashed toward it as before, but now she did not go through the fan, but zoomed up over the top of it. As long as it was on at high speed she would not go through it, but when I turned it back to the lower speed she dashed into the blade again.

I found the pamphlet of instructions that had come with the fan, and read through it. At slow speed the blade made eight hundred revolutions per minute, at high speed twelve hundred. I am not mathematician enough to be able to estimate how fast the white lady had to fly to go through a blade turning at 800 r.p.m., and how much faster to go through one turning at 1200 r.p.m., but I suppose that somewhere between the two speeds lay the limit of her ability. Still, this may not be the answer at all; it may be that at 800 r.p.m. she was sure of herself; she could co-ordinate her passage through the fan with the revolutions of the blade, while at the higher speed her sense of timing was confused.

It was almost nine o'clock now, and I did not want the white lady to miss her evening meal altogether, or to come back to the grotto after the bats had left their hunting grounds for the night. But how was I to get her back? There was not the ghost of a chance that I could catch her; I had left the net in the grotto, and there seemed little likelihood that she would hang herself up to rest, or that she would let me catch her even if she did. Did I dare to open the window and let her fly out? The book on bats had said little brown bats would return to their roosting place after being taken "a number of miles" away; but how far was "a number of miles"? It was about five miles from our home to the grotto; was that more or less than "a number of miles"? Besides the possibility that she could not find her way back, there was also the danger that someone would see her flying through the city, or leaving our window. Still, there was nothing to do but open the window and let her out, for I certainly would not be able to catch her before morning, and in that case my poor mother would have to stay in her room until she was gone. So I opened the window in the dining room, and before I had it up more than a few inches there was a flash of white beside me, and the white lady was gone. She must have known that I was opening the window for her. As I walked away from the window it occurred to me that I had not taken a single picture of her. I had been so interested in watching her fly through the fan that I had forgotten the reason for which I had brought her home.

I went into my mother's room, and found her sitting disconsolately on the edge of her bed, holding her temples with the tips of her fingers. "You can come out now, mother," I said. "The white lady is gone."

She dropped her hands to her sides and looked up at me.

"Well," she said, attempting to seem humorous but

obviously with great seriousness, "I was just coming to the conclusion that if you had to choose between us, the white bat would win."

"Don't be ridiculous, mother," I said as lightly as I could.

But I think she knew, and I know I did, that in the miracle of the white lady lay my key to freedom from the prison of my stagnant, defeated self. And my mother knew then that she would have to let me go.

XII

THE AVERAGE PERSON TODAY, when the subjects of bats occurs to him, immediately thinks of the so-called natural "radar" which enables these animals to fly about in darkness; it will thus seem strange that I have written so many pages about bats without once mentioning this phenomenon. As a matter of fact, I had thought of it many times as I sat in the grotto and outside of it watching the bats. It was one of the attributes that made these creatures seem so mysterious to me. But it was only something I had read about without actually experiencing; I did not see any manifestations of this "radar" in the bats and so I have had no occasion to mention it before. This does not mean that I consider it unimportant, any more than in the case of an author who writes a book about people without once happening to mention their sense of smell.

When I was a boy I read many articles in popular scientific magazines and the Sunday supplements of newspapers, about the bats' "sixth sense." It had been established even then that bats can fly around obstacles without using their eyes, and it was believed that they did this through some sense other than the five known to man. According to Professor Allen's book on bats, "As long ago as 1794, Spallanzani, an Italian, experimented with bats deprived of their sight to see if they could successfully avoid silk threads hung in the room. He satisfied himself that they could, when blinded, still make their way in and out among the threads without touching them. His conclusion that they were guided by some special sense is still widely quoted."

Later experimenters strung thin wires across a room, and, instead of "depriving the bats of their sight," merely covered their eyes with "an opaque mixture of lamp black and glue." They found that the bats could avoid the wires even better with their eyes covered than other-

[134]

wise. But if the bats' ears were stopped up with plaster of Paris, even though their eyes were open, they could not avoid the wires, but kept bumping into them. Professor Allen's conclusion from these facts is that "Evidently the internal ear, with its acute sense of hearing, is the main factor, not only in helping bats to avoid obstacles, but also in aiding them to hear the hum of a passing insect. No doubt it is the echo of vibrations set in motion by air currents that they really perceive."

It is apparent that Professor Allen puts no credence in the theory that a flying bat, instead of depending on air currents to carry vibrations from an obstacle to its ears, may itself utter a series of high squeaks which would bounce off the obstacle and enter its ears, in the manner of radar. He does not mention this possibility, though it was advanced long before the publication of his book. But of course at that time it had not been proved, and I suppose it would never do for a professor at a university to admit that he had knowledge of a theory which had not yet been thoroughly explored by other professors. By implication, however, he does mention the possibility of such a theory when he says that Sir Hiram Maxim, after learning how bats find their way in the dark, "invented a device for detecting obstacles in a ship's path at night or in a fog by sending out vibrations of a low tone from the ship's prow and recording the echo by delicate membranes on board."

Now here, it seemed to me, was a fruitful field for investigation, and one in which I might at last make some real contribution to science. If I could determine definitely that bats either did or did not avoid obstacles in the dark by giving forth some sort of high sounds, which bounced off objects in their path and were reflected back to their ears, I would be adding something important to man's knowledge of the bats. Then the time I had spent sitting in the grotto and just outside it watching the bats would not have been wasted, at least from a scientific point of view. But could I do it? I was no scientist, and did not have a lot of money to spend on equipment. It would take a lot of time, too, and I wanted to be especially careful of my mother since our unspoken clash. Then I remembered—my mother, possibly as a demonstration of annoyance at my preoccupation with the bats, was going in a day or two on a long visit to her sister in California. For the first time in my life I would be free and untrammeled. I could go to the grotto every evening if I wanted to, sleep under the locust tree as often as I pleased, and bring the white lady home with me whenever it suited my fancy.

As the first step in my projected experiment I visited a firm that manufactured radio and sound apparatus.

After talking to a number of employees I was introduced to one of their engineers, and, without going into too many details, explained my problem to him. He was a short, heavy-set young man, laconic, and abrupt of speech. When he heard what I wanted he said with an air of finality "Can't be done."

"Why not?" I asked.

"Too much equipment. You'd need an oscilloscope, an amplifying system, a high frequency microphone, and batteries to operate the whole thing. You'd have to drive one of those big sound trucks right into wherever these damn bats are. I'd forget about it if I were you."

"But I don't want to forget about it. I want to rent or buy the equipment I'll need, and if you're not interested I'll go to some other firm."

He looked at me intensely for a minute, then said, "O.K., we'll work along with you on it. But first there's one little thing we have to know. What frequency do these damn bats broadcast on? Most microphones only pick up the audible frequencies, up to twenty thousand cycles. If the sound these bats broadcast is not audible it must be higher than that. We have to know how much higher before we can supply you with a microphone to pick it up."

So that was my problem, and for a week I wrestled with it. Around and around I went in a sort of vicious circle; since there was no information on the frequencies bats used to send out their sound, it was impossible to know what sort of microphone would pick it up, and unless I used the proper microphone I could not determine what frequencies they broadcast on. I could experiment, of course, using one microphone after another until I heard the sounds, but this was such an unscientific procedure that I hesitated to suggest it to the engineer. After a time I began to wonder whether the engineer himself had known that the problem was insoluble, and had sent me off on a wild-goose chase to get rid of me. But I was determined not to give up until I had tried every possible means of solving it.

There is in our city a library devoted exclusively to technical and scientific literature, and here I spent innumerable hours looking up every reference to bats in scientific books and periodicals. Perhaps somewhere, I thought, I would find some mention of the probable frequencies on which bats send out their sounds. And one day I did find an article that contained the information. It was in an issue of the *Journal of Experimental Zoology*, and was written by two professors in the Department of Biology of Harvard University, Galambos and Griffin. Not only did it give the exact frequencies on which bats broadcast their sounds, but also furnished conclusive proof that these mammals avoid objects in

[138]

their path by sending out a stream of high-frequency squeaks that bounce off the object and return to their ears. So there was no purpose now in making the experiments myself, and I never went back to the engineer to explain.

The experiments conducted by the two Harvard professors used four different species of bats, including *Myotis lucifigus*. The bats were brought into the laboratory, and there subjected to various tests. To determine if they broadcast inaudible sounds while in flight, a crystal detector and a voltmeter were used, rather than the more cumbersome microphone-amplifier-oscilloscope setup the engineer had suggested to me. It was found that all the time the bats were on the wing they were giving forth a stream of supersonic tones with frequencies varying from thirty kilocycles to seventy kilocycles, depending on the species of bat. When a bat's mouth was stopped up so that the tones could not come out it bumped repeatedly into wires strung across the room, and the same thing happened when its ears were plugged so that it could not receive the reflected signals. But whether its eyes were open or sealed shut made no appreciable difference; it could avoid the wires easily either way as long as its ears and mouth were open.

But the experimenters were not satisfied with these tests alone. In order to find out what part of the bats' ears detected the supersonic sounds they attached the volt-meter to various parts of the ear, and found that the high frequency sounds were received in the cochlea. When the voltmeter was attached to this part of a bat's ear there was a rise in voltage every time another bat flew near, or when high frequency sounds were produced artificially by the experimenters. A phenomenon the professors thought interesting, though they could not explain the reason for it, was the fact that the cochlea seemed espe-cially sensitive to supersonic tones just before a bat died. In every case, just before the death of a bat the voltage rose sharply, showing a heightened receptivity for per-haps a minute before death, and then dropped to zero.

Sitting in the grotto on the evening after I had read this article, watching the bats as they circled the tree trunk just before going out for their evening's hunting, I thought of the myriads of supersonic squeaks they were sending out, sounds that were all about me, that filled the grotto like a pandemonium, but which I could not hear. If I possessed a cochlea like the bats, or even an artificial cochlea made up of a crystal detector and a voltmeter, I could learn to identify the squeaks of individual bats. I could pick out the white lady's squeaks from among all the others, just as she herself could identify her own squeaks in that bedlam when they were reflected back

[140]

from some object. As I sat there thinking this over, life seemed very mysterious and unknowable, filled with waves and forces and sounds and movements incomprehensible to me or to any other living being. Three high frequency sounds that whirled around me I knew about, though I could not hear them. There was the supersonic squeaking of the bats; there were the higher frequency sounds sent out by some hundreds of radio stations, carrying music and voices; and there were the ultrahigh frequency sounds sent out by half a dozen television stations, which, with the proper receiving apparatus, would resolve themselves into pictures of men and women, of dancers and singers and actors. But how many waves from other sources were beating against me, how many emanations that might be capable of opening whole new worlds, had I but the proper receivers, were floating all about? It seemed to me at that moment that man's knowledge, all the things he has ever learned and thought and seen and felt, was only an infinitesimal part of the vast area of things knowable.

Until today I had not been sure that the bats avoided each other and obstacles in their path by utilizing supersonic tones, though I had suspected it. But now that I was certain I could look back at some of the things that had happened and understand them better. When for the first time the white lady had flown toward the blades of our fan at home, and then veered up over the top of it, she was sending her supersonic squeaks toward it at the rate of sixty squeaks a second, and the echo that came back to her ears told her exactly how fast the blade was whirling, and whether she could safely fly through it. And when I suddenly pushed my net up in front of her as she circled the tree trunk in the grotto, I was not by any stretch of the imagination trapping her by my quickness or agility. The metal ring around my net reflected her squeaks, but her ears told her that inside the ring was clear, and, as I have discovered from watching the bats, there is some strange quirk in bat mentality, some childish spirit of showing off, that urged her to go through things whenever possible, to fly between two obstacles in her path rather than around them.

What was life like to the white lady, what shape and color did the world have in her perceptions? Her small eyes, even smaller than those of a mouse her size, were, while not altogether useless, only helpful in broad daylight, and even then showed her only vague lights and shadows. She was color blind, I knew that, and the picture her eyes presented to her was that of a drab, colorless, shadowy void surrounding her. But from her mouth she uttered a constant stream of supersonic squeaks, and

[142]

these, reflecting back to her ears, filled out for her a picture of the world. But what sort of world was it that she saw reflected in her mental radar screen? Could she tell what an object was from the squeaks that bounced off it, could she guess what it was made of, and speculate as to its possible uses? Or was her world made up of empty space with here and there an obstacle to be gotten around, like a blind man tapping his cane in a black world?

These are questions that anyone may ask, but no one can answer, for the answers are locked up deep within the consciousness of the bats themselves. Even if it were possible for a bat to explain her conception of things to a man, if they shared a common language, would he be able to understand her, would he be able to conceive of the things she was telling him? A man can only understand something that he has himself experienced, or a thing that approximates an experience he has had. If a friend tells me that he is unhappy, that the world seems bleak and unfriendly to him, I can sympathize with him because I, too, have been unhappy, and have looked out on a bleak and unfriendly world. But how could the white lady, even if she were able to speak to me, convey to me a sense of what it was like to be winging through a forest on a pitch-black night, eyes and ears and other senses shared with human beings of no use to her, receiv-

[143]

ing from the cochlea of her ears a picture of the space before her, of the shape and position of trees and bats and branches and insects?

Science can tell us many things about the other creatures around us, our neighbors on the planet earth; it can give us a detailed explanation of the physical make-up of each species, of how it lives and gets its food and raises its young. But science cannot tell us what it is like to be a bat or an elephant or a fly, it cannot probe into the inner consciousness of a living being and peer into the secret reactions to its existence. And while it is important that science should discover and announce the facts about other living beings on the earth, it seems to me equally important that a man should occasionally step away from his constant association with other human beings, and immerse himself in lives different from his own, steep himself so far as possible in the personality and subjective perceptiveness of other creatures. So that even though I had not alas discovered any new theory about bats, even though I had not been the one to prove that bats find their way in the dark by the use of high frequency sounds there was some consolation in the knowledge that I was closer to the bats in the grotto, more intimate with them and more appreciative of their style of life, than any scientist intent on his experiments

[144]

could ever be. Though the two professors had discovered things that were of value to science, objectively, the things I had discovered by watching the bats were of far greater value to me.

XIII

THE LITTLE BROWN BATS WOULD
return to their roosting place after being taken a number
of miles away, Professor Allen's book had said. I knew
the number of miles was more than five, for the white
lady had returned to the grotto after I let her fly out of
the window of our dining room. The next morning on my
way to work I had stopped off at the grotto, and found
her hanging in her usual place on the roof. How far from
the grotto could I take her without fear that she would

not return, without having her lose her way or decide to go somewhere else to roost?

Toward the end of August I decided to try an experiment to find out how strong was her homing instinct. The grotto was full of bats now, males as well as females, and if I sat on the floor for a few minutes I could feel again the air of tension and excitement I had felt last year when the bats were beginning their courtships. Instead of hanging from the roof of the grotto all day long, to fly up only when I came too close to them, the bats now zipped about under the tree nervously, as though they were particles caught in an electric field. And in truth they had been caught in a field of force, though it was a physiological rather than an electrical field. They were in the grip of the sexual urge, and this strong force plunged them into inordinate action, sent them hurtling after each other through the grotto when they should have been resting.

The white lady had a suitor too, a little brown fellow no different from the others, who hung beside her on the roof, edged toward her at every opportunity, and chased her around the grotto. It would have been interesting, I thought, to know why, and in what manner, he had selected her from among all the other females as the object of his courtship. Did her conspicuous white fur make her especially desirable as a mate, and had the males fought over her, or reserved her for the strongest or swiftest among them? This might be the case, but it was equally possible that the males considered her less desirable as a mate than a female of their own color, and that she had been relegated to the weakest among them.

In order to begin my experiment I waited until the bats were circling the tree trunk just before leaving the grotto, then caught the white lady in my net and put her in the cigar box. Putting the box on the seat beside me in my car, I drove through the crowded city traffic to the south side. I parked the car in Jackson Park and walked with the cigar box to a secluded spot where she would not be observed by anyone else when she flew up into the air. This was about fifteen miles from the grotto. Would she be able to find her way back? If she did not I would never see her again.

I opened the lid of the box a trifle and put my hand in, then brought the white lady out. She did not struggle to escape, nor did she squeak or try to bite my fingers. "Well, white lady," I said to her, "*auf Wiedersehen,* I hope. But if not, then this is good-by." I threw her up into the air and watched her fly off between the trees. As I saw her disappear I said to myself: No, she will never find her way back to the grotto. As a matter of fact, she had flown southeastward, in the direction exactly opposite to where the grotto was. In a minute or two she

[149]

would find herself over the lake, and she would probably fly above the water until she became confused and exhausted, then sink down and be swallowed up by the waves.

As I walked back to the car I was filled with regret. What a fool I was to have taken her so far in the first stage of my experiment. I should have taken her perhaps eight miles at first, then ten, and finally fifteen miles from the grotto. I was even worse than those professors who had killed one bat after another so as to watch the voltmeter needle jump just before each one died; the bats meant nothing to these men, they were merely objects on which to experiment. But there was a bond between the white lady and me. I had watched her being born, seen her grow to adult bathood, and observed her first flight. For her part, she trusted me, she welcomed me to the grotto by diving just over my head as I walked across the field, and she ate insects from my hand. She had been a guest in my home many times, and it was because of her that I had found the courage to declare my independence from my mother. Now, for the sake of a foolish experiment, an experiment which would prove nothing, I had taken her away from her home and her companions and set her adrift in a hostile world.

How could I have been so thoughtless as to believe that she would be able to find her way back from a distance of fifteen miles? It was true that almost any bird could have done it, even a tiny hummingbird. But birds use their eyes to find their way, they will circle high in the air looking for some familiar landmark. A bat cannot use its eyes in this way, it must depend entirely on those high-frequency squeaks which it sends out in a constant stream. I could imagine the white lady flying all night over the lake, sending out those supersonic squeaks and receiving no echo, or, if she was over land, having them reflected back to her ears from strange, unfamiliar objects.

I decided to return to the grotto and wait under the tree, all night if necessary, to see if she returned. Perhaps, through some miracle, she would find her way back during the night, and, worn out with flying, would come to the grotto to hang herself up and rest. So I drove back by the quickest route, and arrived at the grotto at ten minutes to nine, while the bats were still outside hunting insects. And flying about among them, looking not a bit the worse for her experience, was the white lady, her fur tinged with pink from the last rays of the setting sun. I caught a grasshopper and held it up in the air, and she swooped down and took it from my hand, so I knew she was not angry with me for my thoughtlessness.

In due time the white lady accepted her suitor, and I saw them copulating a number of times, hanging from the roof and crawling up among the vegetation. Next year she would become a mother, and then she would have experienced everything that life had to offer a bat, and the remainder of her existence would be but a repetition of what she already knew. What sort of baby would be born to her? I realize that albinism is seldom inherited, but I could speculate on the possibility that she was not an albino, that her white skin and fur was due to mutation in one of her genes. In that case her offspring might inherit the mutant gene, and if it was dominant her child would be as white as she was. But even if her child was not white, if it was as brown as the other bats, it would be interesting to observe her behavior as a mother, to see how she took care of her child. Yes, next year I would continue to watch her, I decided, I would still keep her to myself. Perhaps the year after that I would bring her up to the Museum and let the scientists study her. She would be old by then, and would not have many more years to live anyway.

Toward the end of September I had occasion to drive to Milwaukee on business, and I decided that this was a good opportunity to take the white lady out even further than fifteen miles and see if she could find her way back. But this time I wanted to see how long it took her to fly back to the grotto, and so I planned to leave her in the car while I conducted my business in Milwaukee, and release her somewhere along the route on my way back. Then I could return immediately to the grotto and wait for her to come in, and I would know how fast she had made the return trip.

I came to the grotto early in the morning, while the bats were asleep. They slept more soundly now than earlier in the summer, for the torpor of their winter hibernation was beginning to affect them, and I did not even need a net to catch the white lady. She kept her eyes shut until my hand closed around her, and then she only squeaked once, and, after smelling my fingers, lay quietly in my palm. I put her in the cigar box, and I suppose she slept during the long drive to Milwaukee, and while I was conducting my business there.

Now I was faced with the problem of how far from Chicago to release her. I had no fear now that she would lose her way. I was tempted to let her out at Milwaukee, in which case she would have to fly ninety miles on the return trip. But though I was certain now that she could find her way back, if she took the wrong course or became confused somewhere along the way, it might take her three or four days or a week to come back to the grotto. I decided to take the chance, and see what would happen. I would release her just outside of Milwaukee, then drive straight to the grotto and wait for her. If she did not return by nine thirty, when the other bats left their hunting grounds, I would leave and come back the next morning.

Just outside of Milwaukee I turned off the highway and drove down a side road to the lake. Getting out of the car with the cigar box in my hand I walked down an incline to where the calm waters of the lake lapped gently against the stones on the shore. After looking around to make sure there was no one else about, and to satisfy myself that I could not be observed from the highway, I opened the lid of the box. The white lady was awake, she was standing on her feet and supporting herself on her wrists, and she blinked her eyes at the unaccustomed bright light. There is a popular superstition that bats cannot rise into the air from a flat surface. I know this is not true, for I have seen them rise from the floor of the grotto many times, and the white lady has flown up from a table top in my home. But it is an awkward, difficult process, and a bat much prefers to be hanging by its hind legs when it decides to launch itself into the air. So now the white lady slowly crawled to the side of the cigar box, hooked her thumbs to the top and pulled herself up, then dropped over on the other side and spread her wings and flew off. Straight out over the water she flew, and I could see a series of little dimples on the water where she dipped her tongue in to get a drink. But I did not see her turn, she flew eastward out

[154]

into the lake until her white wings disappeared from my view. I looked at my watch, saw that it was ten minutes past two; then got in the car and started back.

It took me two and a half hours to get back to the grotto, which meant that my average speed for the trip was thirty-six miles per hour. I crawled into the grotto on my hands and knees, as usual, then stood up and waited until my eyes became accustomed to the dim light. Most of the bats were hanging from the roof, but only one had become frightened by my entrance and was circling the tree trunk. There in her usual place on the roof hung the white lady, as calm and unruffled as though she had been there all day, her eyes closed in sleep. She had flown ninety miles over unfamiliar territory in less than two and a half hours, and now she was catching up on her lost sleep.

From this time on the bats became more and more lethargic, they slept more soundly, and many of them did not leave the grotto all night long but continued hanging from the roof in deep sleep. During the first week in October coming into the grotto was a strange experience, as though I had entered a castle in a fairy tale where all the inhabitants had been put to sleep by a magic spell. There was an eerie silence under the tree, and I could walk about among the sleeping bats without a single pair of wings flashing suddenly past my face. Once I picked *crue[l]*

the white lady off the roof, touched her head with my finger, turned her over on my palm, and finally spread her wings out with my two hands before she awoke. Then she flew straight back to her place on the roof and hung herself up again, without a single circuit of the tree trunk.

One afternoon about the middle of October, I came to the grotto and found it deserted. The bats had left for their cave or wherever it was that they hibernated during the winter. I had been there the evening before and the bats had been hanging from the roof, and at about eight o'clock a few of them had flown outside to hunt for insects. But sometime between last night and this afternoon something had happened, a signal had been given or a decision made, and they had left the grotto for their winter quarters.

How strange the grotto looked with the bats gone, like a room in a house that has been kept locked for many years. The musky smell was still there, and I could tell myself that it looked no different than it had on any evening during the summer when the bats were outside hunting. But of course there was a difference, for I knew the bats would not be back until next spring, and so it seemed desolate and forsaken to me. Standing outside I could remember with a nostalgic feeling of sadness, as though it was something that had happened a long time

[156]

ago, how the bats shot out of the opening on the top of the grotto like a puff of black smoke, and how the white lady swooped down to take an insect from my hand, and how beautiful she looked just before the sunset, when her body was pink and her wings gleamed with rays of orange light.

XIV

FOR VARIOUS REASONS, I DID
not go to the grotto all that winter. What was the use
when I knew that the bats would not return until about
the first week in May? Actually I had become so accustomed to going there every evening, that at first I missed
my visits. In the evenings, as I sat at home reading a
book, I would feel myself becoming more and more rest-
less and nervous, as though there was something important I had forgotten to do and could not remember what
it was. But as the weeks and the months went by I became

reconciled to the long winter without the bats, and without seeing the white lady. Not that I ever forgot about her for any length of time; the memory of her graceful form flashing through the air was never far from my consciousness. I would be doing something, perhaps sitting at a desk in my office performing some routine function or reading at home, and suddenly, for no reason I was aware of, my mind would light up with a remembrance of her beauty.

Another reason I did not go to the grotto was that during that winter I met and courted the girl who was later to become my wife. She was intelligent and charming and beautiful, and I fell in love with her the first time we went out together. By April we were engaged to be married. Of course I told her about the white lady, how lovely she was, and some of the remarkable things she could do, and how rare it was to find an albino bat. She acted gratifyingly interested, but I suspect only because of my own enthusiasm. For, as she told me again and again, she did not especially care for bats, the very thought of them made her shudder. But she loved beautiful things; the poetry of Keats, the music of Schubert, the paintings of Van Gogh; she loved the sight of the thin crescent moon in the sky, of violets blooming under the snow, of the wind bending a field of grass. So, I reasoned,

[160]

how could she help loving the white lady, once she had watched her skipping across the evening sky?

On the first Sunday in May, a clear though windy day, with the warmth-laden breeze blowing a hint of the summer to come, I drove alone to the grotto to see if the bats had returned. It was late in the afternoon, about four o'clock, and as I drove up California Avenue, even before I came to the bridge, I knew that something was wrong, and a forlorn feeling of apprehension assailed me. The whole area had changed its appearance. It was flat and bleak and muddy; and where before I could see as I approached the bridge the mound of earth left by a glacier and the little forest of trees behind it, now I saw only a level, muddy plain with big trucks standing about, and a tall crane pointing a grotesque finger into the sky. When I had crossed the bridge and stopped on the other side, my heart sank. There was no longer a mound of earth, no trees or bushes or grass; everything had been torn down and taken away. Where the locust tree had stood, with the grotto around its trunk, there now stood a steam shovel on steel treads, with the point of the great open shovel resting on the earth like the jaw of some huge beast about to fill its mouth with food.

There was no sign of any human being about, but farther up on California Avenue I saw a little wooden building that looked like a watchman's shack, and I went toward it. Inside the shack an old man sat before a crude table playing solitaire with worn, dirty cards. He looked up as I came in. "Can you tell me what they're building here?" I asked.

"Housing project," he said. "Gonna be the biggest on the north side."

"Well, you see I knew this place pretty well before they tore it up. Do you recall a locust tree that grew out there just about where that big steam shovel is standing now?"

"Can't say that I do. There were a lot of trees out there when we started, all had to be pulled up by the crane. Any special reason for asking?"

"Yes, there is. There was a colony of bats lived in that locust tree."

"Bats, eh? Guess they scared 'em out when they pulled the tree up."

"No, they were away for the winter." I tried to keep the emotion out of my voice, to sound unconcerned about the whole thing. "They would have come back this week though, if the tree were still here."

"Then it's a good thing for me the tree ain't here," he said. "I got enough to do keepin' the kids around here from stealing things at night, without worrying about bats gettin' in my hair."

[162]

I left the watchman's shack and walked back to the car. Sitting at the wheel before starting the motor, I looked again at the desolate view which last summer had been the forest of trees, the mound of earth, and the grotto. So this was the end of that tiny bit of wilderness which had survived for so many years in the midst of the city, and this was the end of my association with the bats, and of my friendship with the white lady. Now I would never know whether she had a baby, or how long she would live, or what would happen to her. Time would pass for me, and another sort of time would be passing for her, and neither time would be aware of the other, they would be separate and distinct, like two rivers running beside each other but never intermingling.

What had I really learned from the bats, and from observing the white lady for a whole summer? My fantastic ambitious dreams of two years ago, the first time I sat on the grotto floor after I had fallen in, had certainly not been fulfilled. I had discovered nothing that was new to science, and my two summers of watching the bats had only succeeded in opening up a host of new problems which I had no idea how to solve. Where did the bats go each night after nine thirty, and what did they do there? Where were the males in the spring, while their mates were raising the young? How did the white lady find her way back over ninety miles of unfamiliar territory? I could not answer these questions, but I could not even have asked them two years ago.

And yet I had learned some things. I had learned to know something of the character and the personality of little brown bats. I had learned that they are playful and friendly, that they have no fear of man, and that they love freedom. This was not much to have learned in two years, but there were not many people who knew it, and perhaps no one else in all the world who had discovered it for himself. Most people, like my mother and the old man in the watchman's shack, thought bats malicious, spiteful, savage little animals that deliberately went about frightening people and trying to hurt them. And it is not only the ignorant and the uninformed who believe this. The opinion is shared by many scientists and naturalists. W. H. Hudson, in *The Book of a Naturalist,* tells of walking down a country lane in England one evening, when two "common bats" appeared. They circled around him, making "vicious little stoops at my head as if threatening to strike." He writes of their animosity, of their belligerence, of their fear and resentment of him. But if Mr. Hudson had ever known a "common bat" as well as I knew the white lady, he would have used different adjectives. The bats he saw on his walk were probably as innocent of any feelings of viciousness and animosity and resentment as playful little puppies. Prob-

[164]

ably they were merely indulging in some friendly show-ing off to the first human being they had come across that evening.

And did it count for nothing that for a whole summer I had lived with a thing of beauty; did that not have some bearing on this summation I was making? I had watched the white lady being born, I had seen her grow and develop, observed her first flight, and even had a small part in the molding of her character, in the formation of some of her habits. It was as though I had spent the summer observing the production of a work of art, as though I alone of all the people on the earth had watched it grow from an insignificant beginning to an object of loveliness. So even if I had learned no new facts about bats, nor evolved any theories concerning them, my inti-macy with the white lady had more than justified the time I had spent in the grotto.

And yet, I thought as I started the motor, much as I would miss the white lady, it was probably fortunate for me that the bats were not coming back this year. I was to be married in June, and if, afterward, my wife were to say to me, as so often my mother had done, that it was unnatural for a grown man to leave a good comfortable home to spend the evening with the bats, who knows whether our marriage would have turned out to be the happy one it is?

[165]